Political Aspects of Health Care

Donald F. Lavanty

Political Aspects of Health Care

Navigating the Waters of Conflicting Policy

palgrave
macmillan

Donald F. Lavanty
Healthcare Management and Legal Studies
School of Business and Technology
Marymount University
Arlington, VA, USA

Law Degree
George Washington University
Washington, DC, USA

ISBN 978-1-137-40620-0 ISBN 978-1-137-40283-7 (eBook)
https://doi.org/10.1057/978-1-137-40283-7

Library of Congress Control Number: 2018956285

This Palgrave Pivot imprint is published by the registered company Springer Nature America, Inc.
The registered company address is: 1 New York Plaza, New York, NY 10004, U.S.A.

This book is dedicated to my wonderful and faithful wife Dee Lavanty.

Preface

The United States is the only industrialized nation that has not enacted a government-run or regulated national health insurance system. When the United States passed the Social Security Act in 1935, a proposal to include a national health insurance program was rejected and any governmental action on healthcare was left up to the states. The states focused only on regulating medical practitioners' qualifications and allowed them to enter the marketplace and charge fees for their services, the same as any other market-based service. In the years following the passage of the National Labor Relations Act (1935), many companies adopted union-negotiated contracts containing provisions requiring employers to purchase health insurance to cover their employees' healthcare expenses. By 1950, most major corporations that hadn't unionized began to provide their employees with health insurance coverage in an effort to avoid unionization, effectively establishing the United States' healthcare system as one based upon third-party health insurance purchased by employers to cover the costs of their employees' healthcare. It didn't take long for the shortcomings of the system to emerge.

In 1960, 22 million American workers retired. No longer employed, they no longer had health insurance. More to the point, the third-party payment system did not have the capacity to reimburse the high costs of healthcare for the elderly and the nation reached a political crossroads. If third-party coverage was not available or affordable, should the United States develop a national policy to provide its elderly and vulnerable citizens with a healthcare safety net and reimburse their healthcare costs from the nation's tax base?

In 1965, under the Kennedy and Johnson administrations, Congress enacted the Medicare and Medicaid programs providing federal tax dollars to cover the costs of medical and hospital care for the elderly and the poor, respectively. This publication addresses the political events which lead to the enactment of Medicare and Medicaid as well as subsequent events leading to the United States' current healthcare issues. The publication reviews the struggles of each political philosophy and each legislative attempt to enact healthcare programs reflecting those philosophies. The political struggles are rooted in the disagreement between those who support the origins of our market-based healthcare system versus those who support broadening the role of government to provide a safety net of reimbursement and services to those unable to afford health insurance coverage. Each major initiative since 1965 has tried to establish federal policy to connect these divergent goals. Rather than substantively critique each policy initiative enacted from 1965 to 2010—much scholarship has already been published to that end—the objective of this text is to explore the political atmosphere that existed in each era that enabled those programs to be enacted and highlights the various healthcare policies in light of how they were products of the current political climate rather than compare and contrast them to earlier policies.

As a consultant for healthcare associations working on all the healthcare laws from Medicare, the Health Manpower Act, Budget Reconciliation, Clinton healthcare efforts, and the Affordable Healthcare Act, I had a front-row seat from which to witness the politics and policies motivating each action. I took that knowledge to the classroom and developed the course on the Political Aspects of Healthcare, employing the analogy that these various legislative actions to connect the system are like attempting to build a canal connecting the Amazon and Nile rivers, which would be a long and difficult process. Now, I bring this material and knowledge to you in this text with the goal of examining ongoing efforts to create and maintain a workable solution to the conflicts inherent in our healthcare system from all angles, conflicts that arise due to the nature of our democratic government whereby our healthcare policies change based on the position of the voting majority in Congress at the time any action is taken.

Just as the attempt to connect federal policies and programs with state and private third-party programs is like forging a canal across continents, so too is the attempt to find solutions shepherded by the government that are deemed suitable by the American public. Further complicating this task is the intensely private and personal nature of healthcare in the United

States. The Constitution grants citizens a right to privacy, but it remains an open and hotly debated question as to whether access to quality affordable healthcare is a *right* or merely a *privilege*.

As you make your way through the text, be mindful of how historical events and political philosophies have helped shape healthcare policies. Is there more of a disconnect between the two political parties, or between elected officials and the people they represent? Whose voice and interests have taken precedence in each step of our evolving policies, and what does the representation of these interests say about our political process?

Arlington, VA

Donald F. Lavanty

ACKNOWLEDGMENTS

My sincere thanks to the American College of Radiology and the Government Relations department, the American Society for Clinical Laboratory Science, the Dental Trade Alliance, the Federal Group, the Southern College of Optometry, the Dedicated Professional Health Staffers for the US House of Representatives and US Senate, the dedicated Professional Staff for the Department of Health and Human Services, the School of Business Administration and the Department of Healthcare Management, Marymount University, the wonderful students who always inspired me, to my children and their families, to Karen Pollitz, and to my editor, Charlene Gomes and her family.

Contents

List of Figures

CHAPTER 1

Pre-Medicare

Abstract The 1935 National Labor Relations Act (NLRA) was the first political act that had an impact on healthcare, establishing bargaining rights for employees and ultimately leading to the provision of health insurance via third-party nonprofit entities in the form of Blue Cross and Blue Shield. Two significant changes occurred after World War II: (1) for-profit insurance companies were given openings by state legislative and regulatory action to sell health insurance and provide competition to Blue Cross and Blue Shield and (2) as a result of tax law changes, major companies began providing health insurance to employees. In the late 1950s and early 1960s, concerns about healthcare for the elderly and poor led to the enactment of Medicare and Medicaid under President Johnson in 1965, marking the first time the federal government was directly involved in the US healthcare system. The programs left the determination of medical necessity and delivery of services with physicians and hospitals and the payment process with insurance companies. The chapters ahead demonstrate how the makeup of Congress and the presidency, along with the political climate among the American electorate, shaped healthcare policy decisions.

Keywords NLRB • Blue Cross • Blue Shield • President Johnson • Medicare • Medicaid

D. F. Lavanty, *Political Aspects of Health Care*,
https://doi.org/10.1057/978-1-137-40283-7_1

State Licensing of Physicians

Before 1965, there was little federal involvement in the American healthcare system. State licensing laws controlled when a physician or healthcare professional could practice by requiring graduation from an accredited school followed by successful completion of the state licensing exam. Once licensed, practitioners could charge a fee to individuals seeking healthcare services. Practicing medicine without a license was a crime in every state; however, the practice of state-by-state licensure of qualified medical practitioners was not without its faults. As a policy matter, it provided 50 different ways to license practitioners to receive payment for services; so, a practitioner in Hawaii might not receive the same payment as a practitioner in Virginia for performing the same procedure. Each state gave medical licenses the highest recognition because medical physicians were the most educated people in the field of healthcare. When health insurance came into play, this high regard for a medical license resulted in the belief that medical physicians were the most qualified decision makers for determining the costs associated with healthcare services. When someone other than a medical physician was tasked with providing services, their payment would be determined by a prescription from the medical physician ordering the services.

In the early 1900s, in addition to licensing laws, every state passed statutes and set up processes to regulate companies that sold insurance to citizens of the state. States required an insurance company to put up a sizable surety bond so that people who bought any type of insurance would have a guarantee that the company would be solvent when called upon to pay a claim. When these first insurance laws were passed, states were not looking to regulate *health insurance*, as there was none, but the bond requirement would impact future health insurance programs.

The Dawn of Health Insurance

The first political act that had an impact on healthcare and health insurance was the National Labor Relations Act (NLRA), passed by Congress in 1935. The NLRA allowed the industrial work force to band together in collective bargaining units to negotiate with management over issues subject to mandatory bargaining, including determining the wages, hours, and conditions of employment and the right to strike if an agreement was not reached. The collective bargaining unit led to the formation of unions and provided professional expertise to assist the unit in formulating appropriate arguments to be made on the issues subject to mandatory bargaining. These negotiations on the issue of the conditions of employment led to the development of worker benefits, which provided leverage to the employees. Unions viewed these benefits as a win-win: because of tax advantages to employers, benefit packages would be attractive to the employer *and* employee. Instead of a worker getting a raise of three cents an hour, he would get a raise of a penny an hour plus two cents put into a fund for life insurance.

As a result of the NLRA, almost every industry was subject to the right of employees to organize, bargain collectively, and form labor unions. This led to industries providing subsidies for indemnification for life insurance and later worker's compensation insurance and unemployment insurance. The question for the union advisors became: are there other types of insurance that might be appropriate for us to negotiate in the contract? Several union representatives were aware of a health insurance plan adopted in Harris County, Texas by the Board of Supervisors to reimburse physicians and hospitals for charges for services to the teachers in the Harris county school system in conjunction with the Baylor Healthcare System. Several union representatives reviewed the plan and suggested this type of insurance could be a subject for contract negotiations and become another condition of employment.

This idea put the politics of healthcare front and center across the United States. Since insurance is regulated by the states, approval to sell the product known as health insurance would have to be subject to state approval, either regulatory or legislative, for unions to be able to propose considering it in contract negotiations. When unions went to state authorities with a proposal to have the state approve a health insurance plan, physicians and hospitals became very concerned about the state allowing insurance companies to sell health insurance for fear that control of the healthcare system would shift to the insurance providers, who were primarily publicly traded for-profit insurance companies. Any for-profit corporation in the United States that is involved in interstate commerce has shareholders who look to that company to get dividends via shares of stock. Medical practitioners feared that, if a for-profit company was managing a healthcare program and not making money, there would be reductions to the fees for physicians and hospitals. Concerned that for-profit insurance companies would then be in control of all healthcare payments, physicians and hospitals felt they should oppose union efforts to change insurance laws to allow health insurance products to be sold.

Ultimately, unions and healthcare associations came to a political compromise by suggesting to the states that they allow nonprofit corporations to manage health insurance plans, as was the case in Harris County, Texas, and that the governing boards of the Blue Cross[1] and Blue Shield[2] plans be made up of hospital and physician representatives. This is the first of many political compromises made in the development of healthcare policy. The states permitted the Blue Cross and Blue Shield plans to be authorized to form and sell insurance as a product that could be bargained for as another condition of employment in the contract. The Blue Shield plan would be a not-for-profit indemnifier to pay for the costs of healthcare for physician services and Blue Cross would be the indemnifier to pay for the costs of hospital services.

The key in the compromise was that the insurance company would be a not-for-profit entity, governed by practitioners, removing concerns within the healthcare community of reductions in payment based upon shareholder return on investment. The Blue Cross and Blue Shield state-approved plans then became the program agreed to in the union contract and union employees would now have their healthcare costs paid for as a condition of employment. The impact of this arrangement proved to insulate the employee from true costs of healthcare and offer the healthcare provider with almost a progressive guaranteed payment. The political decision for nonprofit sponsored insurance to become a condition of employment was the first rocket fired in what would become the propellant for dramatic increases in cost and spending for future healthcare services.

A Condition of Employment

A political shift came in 1950. After World War II, the country began to reevaluate its resources and get back to the marketplace that built capitalism. With the election there was President Eisenhower and his platform of "New Republicanism," a philosophy of shifting back toward minimal government interference in the marketplace. The predominant philosophy of government in the United States up to President Eisenhower was that government ought to have an active role in many functions to improve Americans' quality of life.

[1] Blue Cross started in 1910 as prepaid health plans affiliated with group practices in the Western United States. In 1929, Blue Cross plans were developed to cover prepaid hospital care based on a prototype developed by Justin Ford Kimball of Baylor University in Texas.

[2] In 1930, Blue Shield plans began providing coverage for physician services in Buffalo, New York.

Dwight Eisenhower was a war hero and voters viewed him and his message in a positive way. He won the election by a wide margin and carried with him the election of many members of Congress to give his party control of the House of Representatives and Senate. His election also helped carry Republican governors and Republican state legislators whose decisions would have an impact on the policy directions for health insurance.

Supported by Eisenhower's philosophy of new republicanism and open markets, the health insurance market would be broadened far beyond Blue Cross and Blue Shield Plans by a combination of state insurance laws and federal tax laws. The for-profit insurance companies were given openings by state legislative and regulatory action to sell health insurance and provide competition to Blue Cross and Blue Shield. This was aided by major companies adding health insurance as a condition of employment as a result of tax law changes. For example, in 1950, Liberty Mutual Insurance offered major medical plans for extended illness in direct competition to Blue Cross' and Blue Shield's coverage. Employers who were not unionized and sought to avoid a union shop partnered with for-profit carriers to offer employer-provided health insurance. On the national level, Congress under the Eisenhower administration expanded the 1943 tax ruling setting aside employer health payments to allow employee health plans to be tax free and tax deductible for the employer.

States where the legislature supposed the marketplace as the controlling force in the industry began to change their insurance laws and allow for-profits to compete alongside nonprofits. The for-profits decided that the system that Blue Cross and Blue Shield adopted was working, so they followed the same model. As a result, by 1951–1952, almost every major corporation and every company that had a labor union, now, had a third-party indemnification process. Health insurance was part of one's job. It was part of the American way of life, part of what employment was about. According to Michael A. Morrisey's book *Health Insurance*, by 1952, most workers were covered by third-party insurance as a condition of employment and, by 1954, over 60% of the population had some type of health insurance either as part of a union contract or employer-provided health insurance.

The Retired, Elderly, and Poor

In the late 1950s and early 1960s, the nation began to face a new national policy question regarding health insurance. National statistics found that 22 million Americans were about to leave the workforce and enter retirement. The question became what happens to employer-provided health insurance when an employee stops working? Suddenly, there were millions of people asking union stewards and human resources directors about health insurance coverage after retirement. The answer: there will be no coverage. From an insurance perspective the elderly constitute a high risk population: in fact they are the highest risk group possible. And people 65 years old in 1960 were *sick*. They had pneumoconiosis from working in coal mines and in the steel mills. Most were smokers. Many had war injuries. According to the US Department of Health, Education and Welfare's 1963 publication *Vital Statistics of the United States—Volume II Mortality*, retirees weren't likely to live past 66 or 67 years. Their serious illnesses would cost the insurance market large sums of money in the move toward modern medicine. The third-party insurance companies—all of them—didn't have reserves big enough to take care of all the elderly people, so there were no plans available for retirees.

The issue soon made it onto the national political radar screen, thanks to the first-ever televised presidential debates between John F. Kennedy and Richard Nixon on September 26, 1960. While the first televised debate dealt with foreign policy, the second debate focused on domestic policy. The two issues Kennedy raised were civil rights and the role of the federal government in providing protection to the elderly and the poor via their ability to buy health insurance through the Social Security system.

Richard Nixon's view was that the issue of health insurance coverage for the elderly and the poor should be handled at the state level. Since the state licensed physicians and regulated the health industry, the state should determine what kind of coverage ought to be available for the elderly and the poor. Kennedy took the position that the states would never do it, otherwise it would have already been done and the federal government has a responsibility to look after those people who supported the country through World War I, World War II, the Great Depression, and the Industrial Revolution. We needed to find a way for them to get their healthcare costs covered.

Getting Buy-In from Congress and the Medical Community

Upon his election in November 1960, Kennedy recommended to Congress that legislation be enacted to create a safety net in healthcare for the most vulnerable of our population—the elderly and the poor. On

November 22, 1963, the country lost President Kennedy to an assassin's bullet and Vice President Lyndon Johnson was sworn in as President. Johnson was a former Senate Majority Leader who knew the American political system and its ins and outs better than most presidents in the nation's history. He knew the workings of a constitutional majority and how to employ it to get social policy enacted into law. He also knew how to achieve the majorities needed in the House and Senate.

The United States' constitutional system of government is based upon a majority rule. To pass legislation, 218 members of the House need to vote for it, and, in the Senate, 60 votes are needed to overcome a filibuster. President Johnson understood that to make a change in social policy you had to build strong majorities. How do you get strong majorities? You make the law you're putting together attractive to members of Congress and their constituents. For a member of Congress from Detroit, with a large number of automobile workers retiring, he proposed a bill that would cover the cost of health insurance at a federal level for the benefit of the elderly who are just retiring and for the children of the elderly who would otherwise have to pay for their parents' healthcare. At that time, every Detroit retiree and union member supported such a move and would support their Representative to vote for the bill. Likewise, every child of a Detroit retiree would support the bill as they would no longer be responsible for Dad and Mom's healthcare costs. Members of Congress would use the local newspaper to outline the bill Johnson was proposing and would then tell his or her constituents what was happening with the proposed legislation in a speech.

In addition to the individual retiree and his or her family, President Johnson also wanted to establish support for members of Congress from the groups who would be affected by a healthcare law. He did this by inviting the various interest groups, including medical physicians, hospital officials, and insurance company representatives, to the White House to discuss his proposed recommendations to Congress.

At that time both nonprofit and for-profit insurance carriers continued to operate based on a physician's determination of "medical necessity." Insurance did not cover anything unless and until a physician determined there was a medical necessity for a service. Johnson's administration supported the physicians' roles as gatekeepers, saying that until a physician determines there's something wrong with an elderly patient, nothing would happen. Johnson knew they would never vote for him, but he understood that, given their status as stakeholders, this proposal would certainly get their attention because there was a constituency of sick people who needed care that they were going to treat. Johnson understood what physicians were about, and he understood that they were part of the power base in every community; physicians were on the boards of directors of the banks and all the major corporations and they could influence what direction his social legislation might take. Just that slight pause regarding the concept of medical necessity, he thought, might be enough for the medical community not to wage an all-out war against any legislation he put forward regarding healthcare.

President Johnson met with the hospital consultants and told them that his administration wanted the hospitals to take care of the elderly and that he would ask Congress to pass a law that will reimburse the hospitals on a cost basis. In hindsight that decision proved to be a major flaw in the reimbursement process. If you're the administrator of a major hospital in Detroit or Milwaukee or New York City or anyplace and you hear the president of the United States tell you the federal government is going to reimburse the hospital for the elderly who are sick on a cost basis—with the number of elderly who needed care—you know your hospital will have a guaranteed patient flow that will be reimbursed on actual costs that the hospital will submit to a federal health insurance program (to be known as Medicare).

Hospital consultants were advised by the Health Insurance Association that the White House staff wanted third-party insurers to manage the program and use the charges for each locale. New York would be different than Alaska or Montana and the carrier or intermediary would reimburse on the local payment established in that area. In effect, the United States would have nearly 74 insurance companies managing the Medicare program after enactment of the law based upon where the insurer and the beneficiary were located. Whatever the regional payment was for lower New York, they would make to insurers in lower New York. Whatever the regional payment was for Hattiesburg, Mississippi, the program would make to the insurers located there. An insurance company would be chosen for each region and they would reimburse for physician visits and other *services* (which would become known as Medicare Part B) based upon actual charge, prevailing charge and local percentage thereof and all *hospital charges* under Medicare (which would become known as Medicare Part A) would be reimbursed on a cost basis.

The Federal Government Gets Involved

The effort to enact Medicare and Medicaid, as a matter of policy, marked the first time in the history of the nation that the federal government would be directly involved in the US healthcare system. Clearly, however, President Johnson's philosophy was to leave determination of the medical delivery system to physicians and hospitals and the payment process to insurance companies. His interaction with Congress saw the role of the federal government as not to dictate a national healthcare system but to find a means whereby coverage for payment would be developed as a safety net for those outside the private health insurance market and to help develop the appropriate infrastructure to meet the demands of private care and new safety net care. By making sure there were enough hospitals, enough physicians, and enough other kinds of ambulatory services necessary for every American to be able to get care through some form of insurance paying for it.

In 1965, President Johnson proposed the Medicaid and Medicare statutes to Congress, which they adopted. At that time, the United States was spending $46.5 billion on healthcare, or about 4.5% of the gross domestic product (GDP). In 2017, the United States spent about $3 trillion, or 17% of GDP on healthcare. How the United States got to spending three trillion dollars will be traced in the subsequent chapters providing insight into how our domestic healthcare initiatives contributed to that growth and how the nation's fiscal policies attempted to scale back the growth without reducing access to care (Fig. 1.1).

The chapters ahead discuss development of the infrastructure for programs, including the Health Manpower Act, the Hill-Burton Act, the establishment of the National Institutes of Health, and then the attempt at retrenchment based upon fiscal and political change. In each of these chapters we see how the political aspects of the American electorate shape healthcare policy decisions. Throughout each of these political changes, one thing is consistent—all proposed legislation seeks to find a way to make the third-party market-based health insurance system function in tandem with the national system of Medicare and federal/state program of Medicaid or other federal programs. In policy discussions about this attempt, I refer to this as the legislative effort to construct a metaphorical canal between two vastly separate bodies of water—the Nile and Amazon rivers—and each healthcare legislative action tries to find the answer to making the private and public healthcare systems connect to provide the

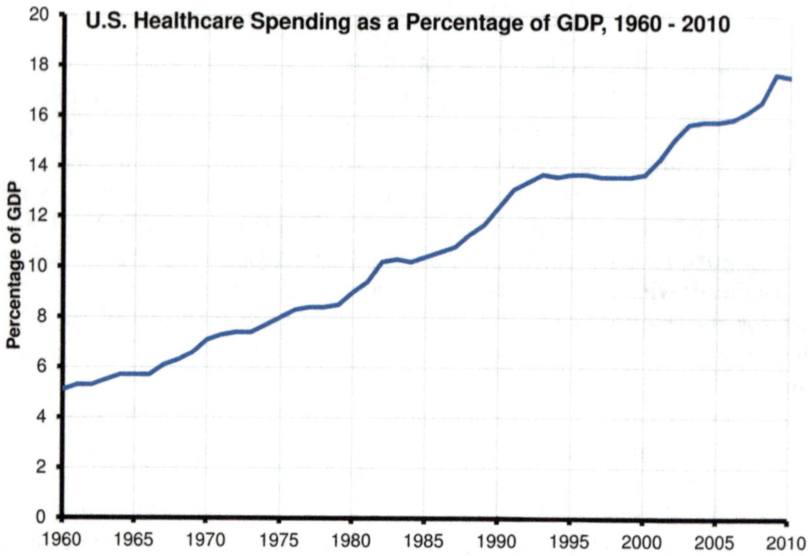

Fig. 1.1 Percentage of GDP spent on healthcare. Source: OECD, http://www.oecd.org/health/healthpoliciesanddata/oecdhealthdata2012-frequentlyrequesteddata.htm, accessed 2012-09-10 18:20

best outcomes to the American healthcare patient. Chapter by chapter, we view the progress on the attempted canal construction.

Following the Winds of Change

Each era's activity is dictated by the politics of the time and the discussion of the various programs and policies enacted, reflecting what the political process allowed. Up through Chap. 4, the emphasis is on the "action" period of healthcare legislation. The politics of Kennedy-Johnson and the electorate acceptance thereof, led to not only the enactment of Medicare and Medicaid, with all their expansions, but allowed Congress to pass significant legislation on healthcare infrastructure legislation. From Chap. 4 on, we see the dynamics of the Kennedy luster wearing off and a congressional recognition that the action period may have been overzealous as costs are again becoming a concern.

The political climate after the Vietnam War led to retrenchment and financial realignment, including a reduction in federal spending on healthcare programs. Veiled attempts were made to deal with healthcare during the Nixon and Carter years, but as I point out in those chapters, the nation's political pulse was one of grave suspicion following the Watergate scandal and deep concern over our military posture as seen in the Iran hostage issue.

Those events led to the ascendancy of the conservative Reagan philosophy where the ideals of a strong military, small government and increased world order caught on and ushered in the era of budget reconciliation which from 1980 to 1990 saw great changes in healthcare delivery and reimbursement. The marketplace was brought to bear on healthcare that was followed in the Clinton years with legislation that fostered a two-way approach. As with the Nixon administration, once again, the political environment of impeachment and policy secrecy left the Clinton administration without any changes in healthcare policy, however, the political climate changed from 40 years of Democratic control to Republican control. Finally, in the last chapter, I examine the winds of political change again with the election of President Obama in 2008, enabling Congress to enact the Affordable Healthcare Act.

Summary

The 1935 National Labor Relations Act (NLRA) was the first political act that had an impact on healthcare, establishing bargaining rights for employees and ultimately leading to the provision of health insurance via third-party nonprofit entities in the form of Blue Cross and Blue Shield. Two significant changes occurred after World War II: (1) for-profit insurance companies were given openings by state legislative and regulatory action to sell health insurance and provide competition to Blue Cross and Blue Shield and (2) as a result of tax law changes, major companies began providing health insurance to employees as a condition of employment. In the late 1950s and early 1960s, concerns about healthcare for the elderly and poor led to the enactment of Medicare and Medicaid under President Johnson in 1965, marking the first time the federal government was directly involved in the US healthcare system. The programs left the determination of medical necessity and delivery of services with physicians and hospitals, and the payment process with insurance companies. The chapters ahead demonstrate how the makeup of Congress and the presidency, along with the political climate among the American electorate shaped healthcare policy decisions. Throughout the text, one theme dominates—

that all proposed legislation seeks to find a way to make the third-party market-based health insurance system function in tandem with the national system of Medicare and federal/state program of Medicaid or other federal programs.

References

Amendments to the Social Security Act, Pub. L. No. 92-603. 1972.

Celebreze, Anthony J., and Luther L. Terry. 1963. *Vital Statistics of the United States – Volume II Mortality Part A*. U.S. Department of Health, Education and Welfare. Source: Centers for Disease Control. https://www.cdc.gov/nchs/data/vsus/VSUS_1960_2A.pdf. Accessed on July 10, 2018.

Health Manpower Act, Pub. L. No. 90-174. 1967.

Hill-Burton Act, Pub. L. No. 79-725, 60 Stat. 1040. 1946.

Medicare and Medicaid, Social Security Amendments, Pub. L. No. 80-97, 79 Stat 286. 1965.

Morrisey, Michael. 2013. *Health Insurance*. 2nd ed. Chapter 1, p. 12. Source: American College of Health Executives. https://www.ache.org/pubs/Morrisey2253_Chapter_1.pdf. Accessed on July 10, 2018.

National Labor Relations Act of 1935, 29 U.S.C. §151–169. 1935.

CHAPTER 2

The Federal Government Enters the Healthcare Field

Abstract Medicare and Medicaid legislation received wide public approval with Americans feeling they were getting a lot from Medicare in return for the moderate increase in their FICA contribution paid into the Social Security system and shared by employers. Adjusting the annual federal income tax to gain revenue to pay for the cost of the federal/state Medicaid program also seemed like a good deal. To make this happen, the House Ways and Means Committee and the Senate Finance Committee worked closely with each other and respected each other's jurisdiction, a level of cooperation rarely seen today. Payments under Medicare were divided into two parts: Part A for hospital payments and Part B for nonhospital payments. The federal government became an additional third-party payer. Unfortunately the data used to determine the funding needed to sustain the programs over time was inadequate and incomplete, resulting in quickly escalating funding deficits that continue even today. Having determined the government has a role in healthcare, Congress began the delicate dance of coming up with policies that would accommodate both systems (and philosophies)—supporting government safety net programs while maintaining a system of private insurance.

Keywords FICA • Social Security • House Ways and Means Committee • Senate Finance Committee • Part A • Part B

D. F. Lavanty, *Political Aspects of Health Care*,
https://doi.org/10.1057/978-1-137-40283-7_2

A Bygone Era of Bipartisanship

Before moving forward to explore post-Medicaid and Medicare enactment changes in US healthcare policy, it's important to take a closer look at the many steps taken and the multitude of players involved in developing the legislation that would become Medicaid and Medicare. The auspicious beginnings of the federal government's involvement in developing and implementing healthcare policies lay the foundation for all future amendments, debates, spectacular failures, and shaky victories in the healthcare arena.

After bringing the major stakeholders into the White House to begin the political process of getting the congressional constituencies of physicians, hospitals, and insurers to become aware of what his administration was considering, President Johnson was prepared to take the next step by proposing legislation that would amend two major federal laws. One would be the Social Security Act and the other the income tax laws to cover the costs of the Medicare and Medicaid programs. Social Security would be amended to increase the Federal Insurance Contributions Act (FICA) contribution to the Social Security trust fund of both employers and employees. This fund covers the cost of hospital care and shares the cost of physician care for people 65 and older and for people deemed disabled under the Social Security system. The annual federal income tax would be adjusted to gain more revenue to pay for the cost of the federal/state Medicaid program and the infrastructure changes needed to support the healthcare system to educate more health practitioners, build more hospitals, and establish federal research centers on diseases. As an initial step, President Johnson would have to deal with the tax writing committees—the House Ways and Means Committee and the Senate Finance Committee—to get them to agree with the concepts of the Medicare and Medicaid programs and the funding mechanisms to support them.

In 1965, the US Congress was organized under a strong committee system. Committee members were experts for the whole US House on matters of jurisdiction before their committee. Once a committee came to a consensus on an issue, usually the rest of Congress would go along. President Johnson had the task of getting the chairs of those committees to understand, agree with, and support his concepts. In 1965, the Chairman of the US House Ways and Means Committee was Congressman Wilbur Mills (D-AK), who was, next to the House Speaker, the second most powerful member of the House. As the experts in tax and Social

Security funding, Mr. Mills and his committee would have the responsibility of drafting legislation to develop an insurance program for the poor and elderly, acceptable to the members of the US House.

Unlike other committees in the House, legislation originating in the Ways and Means Committee that is proposed and passed by the entire House of Representatives needs no further legislation in the House to cover the costs of the program—the tax writing committee can authorize and fund the legislation out of the tax system. Therefore, the provisions passed in the House, if enacted and agreed to in the Senate were automatically funded through the FICA tax for Medicare and the federal portion of the Medicaid program would be funded out of the general income tax.

Committees respected each other's jurisdictional boundaries and did not traffic on the authority of the others. Once a committee brought a bill to the floor of the House of Representatives, the House usually voted for it. For example, the House Armed Services Committee would put all their trust in the House Ways and Means Committee's legislation and vice versa. There was trust in each committee's action because those committees had followed a rigorous process of exercising hearings and vetting the law. Furthermore, each committee had members from every region of the country who were experts on every subject of the Congress. The Congress relied on the committee structure and the mutual trust it fostered. Committee Chairs wielded a lot of power, and one of the most powerful people during the enactment of Medicare was Wilbur Mills. Of note is the fact that, notwithstanding its major amendments, the basis of American tax law was written by Rep. Mills.

In the US Senate, Russell Long (D-LA) was Chair of the Senate Finance Committee, which had jurisdiction for Social Security, tax, and FICA. Prior to becoming John F. Kennedy's running mate, Lyndon Johnson was the Majority Leader of the Senate, where he and Senator Long were close political and personal allies. The Medicare and Medicaid proposals were the first issues addressed by the House Ways and Means Committee and the Senate Finance Committee, which were jointly tasked with overseeing legislation funded out of the tax system. The Medicare and Medicaid legislation passed in the US House of Representatives, but there were significant differences with the US Senate, requiring a conference committee to work out the differences between the respective bills.

One of the major disagreements between the House and Senate recommendations was payment to hospital-based physicians. Hospital-based physicians include radiologists, anesthesiologists, and pathologists and are referred to as the RAPs. The Senate had them as part of the hospital structure and reimbursed under Part A. The rationale was that if the service the physician was providing to the elderly patient was carried out in the hospital, the service should be paid as part of the hospital service. Those physicians would in effect be employees of the hospital. The American Medical Association (AMA) had so many issues to deal with in the legislation that they advised those groups of physicians to seek independent representation to keep them from being included as in-hospital payers. The American College of Radiology (ACR) retained a former member of Congress, who had a close relationship with Wilber Mills. He called upon a radiologist from Arkansas to accompany him to meet with Rep. Mills and his aide Bill Fullerton to request that the Medicare law treat the RAPs under Part B for payment—the same as all other physicians.

The House bill already had the services provided by RAP physicians to beneficiaries, while in the hospital it was billed under Part B as physicians' services. The legislative group retained by ACR was able to convince the Senate staffers, especially Jay Constantine, to accept the House version and give those doctors the same payment as all other Part B physicians, with the admonishment that if the hospital-based physicians engaged in percentage arrangements with the hospitals (a way to get 100% reimbursement) then the Finance Committee would reassess the provision. They made good on this promise to prohibit hospital-based physicians from having a Part A percentage arrangement with the hospital by adding a provision to the Tax Equity and Fiscal Responsibility Act (TEFRA) in 1982.

The 1965 Medicare payment decision of dealing with those physicians generally not seen in the hospital under Part B relates directly to present-day debates over the surprise medical bills patients sometimes receive from emergency room doctors and others that work at hospitals, but bill independently. With the Congress demanding that hospital-based physicians bill under part B, these bills are usually unexpected and from a doctor that the patient usually does not get to choose.

Public Reaction to Medicare and Medicaid

Congress agreed to the conference report and the Medicare and Medicaid legislation was signed into law on July 30, 1965, by President Johnson resulting in a major shift in American healthcare policy by adding direct federal involvement in the US healthcare system. The law (1) provided reimbursement for people over the age of 65 for hospital coverage

(Medicare), (2) shared reimbursement for physicians' services, and (3) developed a federal-state tax sharing program for reimbursement of the costs of healthcare services for certain persons below the poverty level (Medicaid). Medicaid recipients were—at the time—the "sympathetic" or "deserving" poor, including mothers and children receiving cash assistance. Later chapters will discuss efforts to expand Medicaid to cover others living below the poverty level. There were exclusions under the law that would result in subsequent action by healthcare groups to secure coverage and payment for their services, such as optometrists, physical therapists, audiologists, and other practitioners referred to as "allied health practitioners." There would also be a major restructuring of the law in 1983 regarding payment for hospital services from retrospective to prospective payment.

Unlike the reaction of the American electorate to presidents Clinton and Obama healthcare reforms and the instant news analysis of today, the enactment of Medicare and Medicaid was politically well received. Members of Congress in 1965 were able to outline for their constituents the advantages of the program: coverage for mom and dad's care and coverage for them when they retired, all provided by a moderate increase in the FICA contribution paid into the Social Security system by employers and employees. This resulted in a high instance of reelection of sitting members of the Congress, including the US House maintaining a 61-seat margin as documented in "Statistics of the Congressional Election of November 8, 1966."

With the reelection, members of Congress and the Johnson administration, both under Democratic control, saw this as a signal that involvement by the federal government in the heretofore private third-party health insurance system was appropriate if the federal programs did not interfere with the working electorate's work-related healthcare coverage. The payment formulas adopted in Medicare Part A and Part B was patterned after the private health insurance payment system. Medicare Part A followed Blue Cross for hospital payments and Blue Shield for Part B payments. These formulas had been used and adopted by the providers and payers of the Medicare program and were politically acceptable in that they just added the government as another third party payer.

The test for the returning members of Congress would be how they could craft federal healthcare policy in a way that would not take American healthcare toward a system of universal healthcare as a condition of citizenship, as in Canada or Great Britain. In other words, come up with a policy to allow both systems (government safety net programs plus private insurance) to function. The political reality was that to get majority buy-in, there had to be a recognition of both factions—marketplace and healthcare as a right. Some advocates wanted the universal access to care for all approach, but that is not possible in our system. Therefore, what is possible is to find the compromise. Subsequent chapters will discuss how Congress set about this effort to improve the infrastructure of the healthcare system without altering the basic insurance structure, such as passing laws to expand and build hospitals, expand educational programs to train healthcare providers, and fund the research to overcome diseases and not move to a universal system.

Figuring Out Funding

As popular as the legislation was, implementation was not without its challenges. The infrastructure programs to train personnel and build hospitals were within the jurisdiction of the individual House and Senate committees that dealt with programs authorized under the Public Health Service Act. The House committee of jurisdiction for those programs was the Interstate and Foreign Commerce Committee (now the Commerce Committee) and in the Senate, the Labor and Public Welfare Committee (now the Health, Education, Labor and Pensions Committee or HELP). In both the House and Senate, unlike the Ways and Means and Finance committees, these committees could only authorize legislation and set up a suggested amount for funding of the program. Program funding would then have to be determined by a third layer in Congress referred to as the appropriations committees. The appropriations committees would review all authorized legislation (aside from those regarding taxes or Social Security) and then determine how much money would be allotted for funding those programs.

In a highly structured Congress with members respectful of the jurisdiction of each committee and the need to fund so many different programs, to say that there would be confusion as to healthcare policy is an understatement. The tax committees set the bar for the coverage provisions of the Medicare and Medicaid programs, the Commerce and HELP committees set the authorization for the Health Professions Educational Assistance Act, Hill-Burton, and the National Institutes of Health (NIH) and the appropriations committees would have the final say of how much would be allocated for the authorized non-Medicare and Medicaid programs. Each of these congressional committees were healthcare policy fiefdoms of their own and until the mid-1970s, healthcare was determined by three various sections of the House and Senate.

On the specific financing of the Medicare and Medicaid programs, the administration and the Ways and Means and Finance committees agreed on a slight increase in the Social Security FICA contributions of both employers and employees. Under actuarial data available in the 1960s, it was projected that the increase in the FICA amount would not only cover the healthcare costs of the elderly but would be sufficient to establish funding for future generations. Hypothetically, for each dollar of FICA, 50 cents would go into payment for coverage of care for the elderly and 50 cents would go into the Social Security trust fund. In theory, as the Johnson administration and Wilbur Mills saw it, the working employees providing the dollar would have fifty cents of it set aside for when they retire. Therefore, the estimated cost of elderly healthcare by 1972 would be approximately $700 million, however, the real cost of Medicare by 1972 was $13 billion. Not only did the 50 cents "saved" for the worker's retirement disappear, but in addition, FICA contributions would have to be increased to cover the $13 billion, constituting the first of many healthcare budget misfires.

This misfire on actuarial projections was a major policy mistake. But what actuarial data was available? The Social Security actuarial looked at past costs and risk to determine what future costs would be. The data available to project future healthcare costs, as in all insurance is based upon risk. For example, in automobile insurance, the age of the driver will determine his or her loss ratio and the projected loss and hence the premium. In 1965, Wilbur Mills, Senator Long, and President Johnson agreed on the needed FICA increase based upon the actuarial data. Unfortunately, the only data available at the time was that of a healthy population. The data looked at the people who were between 18 and 50 and who seldom used the healthcare system except to take care of their children or for treatment of a major illness, and therefore the expenditure was approximately 25 cents on every dollar. Also, the projections were that only 25% of the 22 million Americans would use Medicare. They put all this together and came up with a figure of $700 million and increased the FICA contribution to represent that amount. Congress believed the plan had been funded for coverage and would look to the legislative committees for programs to deal with the infrastructure of healthcare funded by income tax dollars (which are separate from FICA tax) to fund education, construction of hospitals, and research on disease.

In addition to the funding issues under Medicare and Medicaid, a constant political and legislative struggle ensued over the next 40–50 years on how to make the programs still provide the benefits authorized with enough revenue remaining to reimburse for coverage.

The benefit package authorized by the Medicare and Medicaid statute included authorized payment for hospital services on a cost basis. President Johnson and Congress adopted the Blue Cross formula utilized by both union plans and private third-party insurance. The formula was known, liked, and seemed to work.

On the Part B side, which covers nonhospital services and supplies deemed medically necessary to treat a patient's health condition, including outpatient care, ambulance services, and durable medical equipment, Congress limited payment for coverage of physician services on the same formula adopted by the Blue Shield programs (paying a percentage of the prevailing charge for providers performing a specific procedure within a single geographical area), while allowing physicians to update their actual charge on an annual basis. From 1965 to 1972, for physicians to receive more reimbursement for Medicare services, the percentage of the prevailing charge would have to increase. Not surprisingly, data shows (see Fig. 2.1) that for every annual update the actual charges increased. Congress also set limitations on which practitioners could be reimbursed under Part B. The definition of a physician under Section 1861(r) of the Social Security Act in 1965 only covered a medical doctor, osteopathic doctor, or, in limited circumstances, a dentist. To be eligible for Medicare reimbursement, any other practitioner would have to have a physicians' prescription to provide the service. This decision would lead to many political debates that Congress would have on whether to add additional practitioners for direct coverage. It would also lead nonphysician groups to work both locally and nationally to develop support for their inclusion under the Medicare program as participating providers.

Summary

Medicare and Medicaid legislation received wide public approval after being passed into law on July 30, 1965. Americans felt they were getting a lot from Medicare in return for the moderate increase in their FICA contribution paid into the Social Security system and shared by employers. Adjusting the annual federal income tax to gain revenue to pay for the cost of the federal/state Medicaid program also seemed like a good deal. To

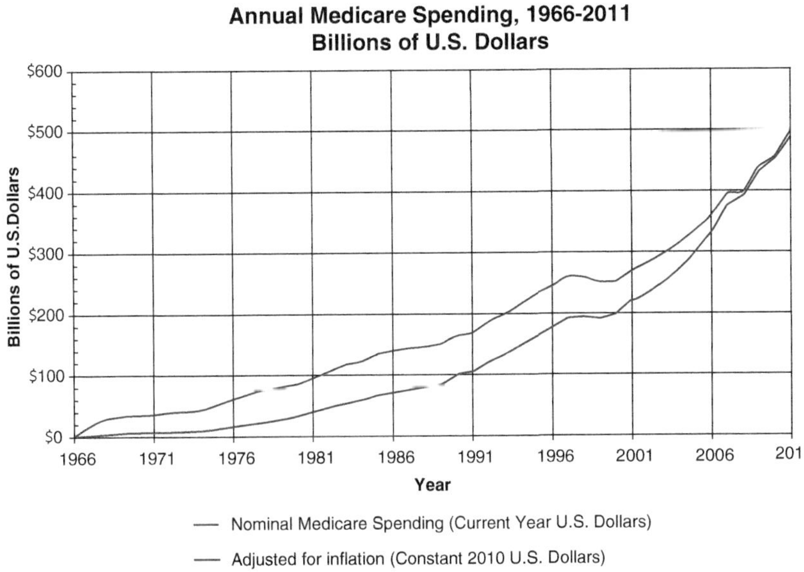

Fig. 2.1 Skyrocketing Medicare costs show no signs of slowing down. Source: White House Office of Management and Budget, Budget of the United States Government FY 2012, Historical Table 3.2 and author's calculations

make this happen, the House Ways and Means Committee and the Senate Finance Committee worked closely with each other and respected each other's jurisdiction, a level of cooperation rarely seen today. Payments under Medicare were divided into two parts: Part A followed Blue Cross for hospital payments and Part B followed Blue Shield for nonhospital payments. In essence, these formulas simply added the government as another third-party payer. Unfortunately the data used to determine the funding needed to sustain the programs over time was both inadequate and incomplete, resulting in quickly escalating funding deficits that continue even today. Having determined the government has a role in healthcare, Congress began the delicate dance of coming up with policies that would accommodate both systems (and philosophies)—supporting government safety net programs while maintaining a system of private insurance. Going forward, the challenges would grow to include the need to develop infrastructure and provide funding to expand and build hospitals, expand educational programs to train healthcare providers, and fund the research to cure diseases.

References

Amendments to the Social Security Act, Pub. L. No. 92-603. 1972.

Guthrie, Benjamin J., and W. Pat Jennings. 1967. *Statistics of the Congressional Election of November 8, 1966*. Source: Clerk of the House of Representatives. http://clerk.house.gov/member_info/electioninfo/1966election.pdf. Accessed on July 10, 2018.

Health Professions Education Assistance Act, Pub. L. No. 88-128, 77 Stat. 164. 1963.

Hill-Burton Act, Pub. L. No. 79-725, 60 Stat. 1040. 1946.

Medicare and Medicaid, Social Security Amendments, Pub. L. No. 80-97, 79 Stat 286. 1965.

Tax Equity and Fiscal Responsibility Act, Pub. L. No. 97-248. 1982.

CHAPTER 3

The Action Period of Healthcare Legislation

Abstract With Medicare and Medicaid in place, Congress set about determining how to properly staff the medical community to meet the needs of patients. Continuing to work in a spirit of bipartisan collaboration, it determined that there was a shortage of physicians, osteopathic doctors, and dentists. Passage of the Health Manpower Act and the Hill-Burton Act provided incentives for medical education and the construction of hospitals and other medical facilities. The result was an explosion in the number of medical specialists (encouraged by the areas of funding/study undertaken by the newly established National Institutes of Health), a lack of primary care physicians, and difficulty attracting medical professionals to rural areas. Amendments to Hill-Burton helped to address some of these issues, making it easier for hospitals to hire foreign-trained primary care physicians and providing incentives for rural areas to build facilities, hire physicians, and provide services to the poor. Conversely, in large cities where Hill-Burton funds were used for expansion, technology and services were being duplicated from hospital to hospital. Two additional amendments, the Comprehensive Health Planning Program and the Regional Medical Program, helped to consolidate regional services and led to the development of specialty clinics across the country.

Keywords Health Manpower Act • Hill-Burton Act • Allied Health Professions • National Institutes of Health • Vietnam War

D. F. Lavanty, *Political Aspects of Health Care*,
https://doi.org/10.1057/978-1-137-40283-7_3

Staffing the Healthcare Industry

The appropriations process is generally referred to as dividing the pie of discretionary tax funding—funding for defense, environment, education, health, and all other programs funded by the government. After the passage of Medicaid and Medicare, Congress undertook two major pieces of legislation to provide the infrastructure needed to support them, enacting the Health Manpower Act in 1968 and reauthorizing the 1946 Hill-Burton Act.

It remained to be determined whether Medicare was equipped to handle the inclusion of 22 million elderly, and whether Medicaid could provide coverage for the poor of each state. To determine the amount of healthcare practitioners needed to meet the demand, Congress drew on its experience with the Secondary Education Act (SEA), where they needed to provide a sufficient number of schools and teachers. In the case of the SEA, Congress arrived at the amount of schools and teachers needed by reviewing national census data, determining the number of school-aged children and asking education experts if the existing number of schools and teachers was adequate. If not, then funding was needed to increase the number of schools and teachers to meet the need. With the Medicare and Medicaid programs now in full force, that same question was asked of the healthcare system—are there enough providers to meet the demand created by the new federal programs?

There were few experts who had attempted to calculate an accurate ratio of physicians to patients that would meet the medical needs of a given population. The leading information on physician education was derived from Dr. Abraham Flexner, an American Medical Association (AMA) supported educator with the Carnegie Mellon Institute. According to Dr. Flexner's findings regarding the ideal ratio of physicians to patients in the United States, including patients covered under Medicare and Medicaid, it was determined that there was a shortage of physicians, osteopathic doctors and dentists.

Incentivizing Education

Legislative authorization from the congressional committee with jurisdiction over this subject matter was required to fund an effort to increase the number of trained physicians. Jurisdiction fell under the Public Health Service Act overseen by the House Commerce Committee and Senate

Health, Education, Labor and Pensions (HELP) Committee. The legislation developed was named the Health Professions Educational Assistance Act. As originally enacted, the law would provide authorization for federal tax monies to be appropriated for three major categories of funding: (1) student loans for medical, dental, and osteopathic education, (2) construction funding for schools and colleges of medicine, dentistry, and osteopathy to expand or build new facilities, and (3) capitation funding, which was tied to enrollment. Schools that agreed to increase enrollment to overcome the shortage identified by the Flexner data would receive funding on a per-student basis. Politically, passage of such legislation was not difficult as every state had a medical and dental school and their congressional delegation would be in favor of enactment.

At the same time the Health Manpower Act was passed, Congress was authorizing funding for the National Institutes of Health (NIH) for research on major diseases such as cancer, heart disease, and stroke. This action is important because it influenced the medical schools, residency, and fellowship programs to gravitate toward specialty education based upon NIH's areas of research. As a result of capitation funding coupled with the creation of NIH and its institutes, there was an influx of medical specialists and a reduction in the number of primary care physicians.

The Health Manpower Act (HMA) also led to the expansion and political activity of nonmedical practitioners including optometrists, podiatrists, pharmacists, veterinarians, and nurses. These professions, referred to as the "allied health professions" and "nursing profession" successfully lobbied Congress using the same Flexner arguments of there being shortages of practitioners, to amend the HMA in the early 1970s to include these professions under the three areas of funding. In discussions with congressional staff on the authorizing committees, the funding became known as funding for medicine, osteopathic medicine, and dentistry (MOD) and veterinarians, optometrists, podiatrists, and pharmacists (VOPP). Lobbying discussions revolved around how much funding would be allocated for the MODs, the VOPPs, and nursing. Every healthcare practitioner group developed, expanded or retained staff to lead these lobbying efforts and most of the professional associations also developed Political Action Committees (PACs) to fund congressional members' reelection efforts and gain lobbying access for their positions on the manpower legislation.

At this time, the AMA saw a crack in its political influence due to the activity of the Association of American Medical Colleges (AAMC), which viewed the HMA as a positive program that would provide more funding to grow their schools and educate more practitioners. Conversely, the AMA wanted to keep the growth in the number of new professionals at a much slower rate. The two associations often had different views on the HMA.

Another important aspect during the early formation of Medicare, Medicaid, and the infrastructure programs of the Public Health Service Act was the bipartisan nature of the Congress. Both Democrats and Republicans, while sometimes having minor disagreements, worked together to craft and pass the legislation. On the Senate HELP Committee, the staff would jointly develop the legislation. At the time, Senator Ted Kennedy (D-MA) was Chair of the Health Subcommittee of the Former Senate Labor and Public Health Committee. His Chief of Staff, Lee Goldman, who was the majority staffer as the Democrats controlled the Senate, worked very closely with the minority, Senator Jacob Javits (R-NY) who was the ranking Republican on the Kennedy Health Sub-Committee. The bipartisanship was so strong that it was not unusual for staffers to transfer from a Democratic senator to a Republican senator's staff. One of Senator Kennedy's legal counsels on the committee with Mr. Goldman and Jay Cutler, Senator Javits' counsel on the subcommittee, was Alan Fox. Mr. Fox later became the Chief of Staff of Senator Javits. The bipartnership contributed greatly to the advancement of many of the healthcare programs.

Geographic Disparities and the Rise of Specialists

As the medical schools and residencies educated more specialists, a growing trend of medically underserved areas was developing. While the intent of the HMA was ideally to educate more physicians to fill the needs of all communities, in reality, the increase in specialty education and increased reimbursement of specialists over primary care physicians resulted in the majority of newly educated specialists practicing in high-density urban centers. Specialists rely upon a large volume of patients to be successful and a medically underserved area with a population of 12,000 or less was not attractive to a new resident trained under the HMA as the need for their services would be limited.

The HMA's goal was to supply the resources to educate enough physicians and other practitioners so that every area of the country would be able to provide adequate care. The growth in specialists prevented that and Congress had data showing a shortage of providers in many underpopulated areas. To address this, Congress adopted several amendments to the HMA. The first, as mentioned above, expanded available funding to include allied health schools (including those training technicians and technologists in many areas, i.e. x-ray, laboratory technicians, etc.). The second major amendment to attract physicians to underserved areas was a loan forgiveness provision. If a physician agreed to practice in a designated medically underserved area for a specified term of years, any outstanding student loans would be forgiven at the end of the term. Very few new specialists availed themselves of the loan forgiveness program as they could earn more by working in a populated area and pay off the loan anyway. The failure of physicians to participate in the forgiveness plan provided an additional argument for the nonmedical providers (i.e. that their education programs should be eligible for all three provisions of the HMA). The third major amendment was to require all schools and colleges to set aside slots for minority recruitment, including women and people of color in order to be eligible for program funding. This followed the federal pattern of the civil rights concepts in all federally funded healthcare programs.

The fourth amendment came in the early 1970s and established the National Health Service Corps (NHSC). This would allow physicians and other limited practitioners to be eligible to serve in a medically underserved area by working in a federally funded clinic while receiving both loan forgiveness and a stipend based on pay for a military rank of 03 (roughly the equivalent of a General Schedule 12–13 for civilian federal employees), the pay of a Captain in the Army and substantial reimbursement for a starting salary physician to serve in an underserved area. This program initially was very successful given its implementation during the Vietnam War. During the war, physicians, dentists, and optometrists and graduates of these programs were subject to a military doctor's draft, but if a physician or other practitioner agreed to serve in the NHSC, their participation counted as military service, exempting them from the draft.

The NHSC was initially a political and policy success, attracting medical providers to underserved areas. Once the Vietnam War ended and their tour was over, many physicians left the corps and the country was again faced with shortages in low-population areas. The shortage provided political leverage for allied health providers such as optometrists to lobby for inclusion in all federal healthcare programs. These allied health providers had two main arguments. First, they argued that because their practitioners were often located in small communities their services should be covered under Medicaid and Medicare. Second, because they had been successful at the state level in expanding their licensed scope of practice to include the provision of topical drugs and first-level eye care if the rural area did not have a physician, they felt they should be eligible for all the provisions of the HMA.

The key major medical decision made by Congress and President Johnson was that a licensed physician must certify "medical necessity" in order for there to be reimbursement to a hospital for providing services. If a small rural hospital serving 12,000 people with a 25-bed capacity built by Hill-Burton Act funds treated elderly or Medicaid patients, reimbursement would only occur if there was a licensed physician to certify medical necessity. Since there were no primary care physicians to practice in that setting, rural hospitals had to find a way to attract physicians to practice in the area. They decided to use the immigration provision of the Immigration and Nationality Act of 1965 to sponsor a nonresident physician to practice at the hospital. The hospital would petition the Department of Labor for certification and demonstrate they were unable to recruit and retain an American-educated physician to practice in the area and ask to sponsor a foreign-born or foreign-educated medical graduate who would sit for a residency in primary care and be the physician for the hospital program. Between 1969 and1976 hospitals sponsored 150,000 foreign-born or foreign-educated physicians so that hospitals could attain cost-base reimbursement from the Medicare and Medicaid programs.

Along with Senator Long on the Medicare and Medicaid programs, Senators Kennedy, Javits, Harrison Williams (D-NJ), Ralph Yarbrough (D-TX), and Herman Talmadge (D-GA) and their staffs began to take a great interest in the HMA and Hill-Burton healthcare programs. In the House of Representatives, along with Chairman Mills of the Ways and Means Committee, Representatives Paul Rogers (D-FL), Tim Lee Carter, MD (R-KY), and Claude Pepper (D-FL) of the Commerce Committee and their staffs were also beginning to engage in those programs.

While the HMA was being put together as part of the infrastructure policy to address the shortages of practitioners, another program receiving congressional attention was the Hill-Burton Act. Passed in 1946, Hill-Burton provided hospitals, nursing homes and other healthcare facilities grants and loans for both construction and upgrades. In return, the facilities had to provide a specified volume of services to the poor and to make their services available to all persons residing in the facility's area. The Hill-Burton program was receiving renewed political attention from hospital associations as well as small towns and communities as they saw the program, along with Medicare and Medicaid cost reimbursement, as an opportunity to build a hospital facility in their area.

The Hill-Burton Act Construction Boom

With the enactment of the HMA, Congress finally made the judgment that the federal government had a role in influencing the infrastructure of the US healthcare system. Shortly after its passage, the members of Congress who supported the legislation found themselves being lobbied by the American Hospital Association, the Catholic Hospital Association, and various state and local associations who represented state and local governments to provide federal funding for hospital construction. Those associations, buoyed by the cost reimbursement policy of Medicare and the provision of tax dollars for the states to fund healthcare programs for the poor, began to ask their Senators and Representatives to consider such programs. They brought Hill-Burton to the attention of the congressional committees of jurisdiction and argued that given the enactment of Medicare and the allocation of shared tax dollars with the states to cover the cost of healthcare for persons below the poverty level, combined with the increase in health manpower, states and local areas needed more facilities to care for these expanded populations.

Initially, Hill-Burton was not very successful because once federal construction monies were expended, the local towns and cities did not have the tax resources to keep those facilities operating with the intent of caring for the poor. With the enactment of Medicaid and Medicare together with the HMA, Congress reauthorized the Hill-Burton Act. The law would provide for federal funding to communities to construct or expand hospitals again, with the requirement that they provide care for the poor and uninsured. This time, along with federal funding for construction, hospitals had the added advantage of the Medicare and Medicaid programs to reimburse them for their services on a cost basis. If a community looked at its demographics and saw a sufficient Medicare population, they saw the connection between the two programs—if private pay did not cover the cost of operation and the community hospital had a Medicare census, the hospital could shift the cost to the Medicare patients to cover the shortfall. The hospital would have its monthly operating cost and whatever the private pay did not cover the remaining costs would be divided among the charges for procedures for the Medicare and Medicaid patients.

In testimony before the Senate Finance Committee in the late 1970s, it was shown that using this method of reimbursement the cost for an aspirin per Medicare patient was nearly $400.00. Which is why, based on this type of testimony and data received on the charge and cost information based upon retrospective reimbursement, in 1983, Congress embraced and enacted a major amendment to the Medicare program referred to as the Diagnosis-Related Groups (DRG).

From 1968 to the mid-1970s, the number of hospitals in the United States increased from about 1700 to 7400, many of which were rural 25–30 bed facilities. They were constructed with federal monies and operated on the cost reimbursement model. The revival of Hill-Burton was very well received. Every Senate and House member supported the program because their state or district, under the right circumstances, would receive Hill-Burton funding. The members of Congress during this period did not have the data yet to assess the impact of Medicare cost reimbursement, so favoring continued funding for Hill-Burton was a political win for sitting members.

In the mid-1970s the Hill-Burton program underwent a series of changes. Congressional staffers did not see the original objective of adding facilities to meet patient needs as being fulfilled. The data was showing rural areas still lacked the number of primary care physicians needed to practice in their area. In large cities, where Hill-Burton funds were used for expansion, services were being duplicated from hospital to hospital. With the advent of new medical technology (e.g. the computerized tomography (CT) scanner or 20 channel clinical lab blood analyzer), every hospital in a 30-mile radius had the same expensive cutting-edge equipment.

Congress discussed, proposed, and enacted two major amendments to the Hill-Burton Act in 1974: (1) the Comprehensive Health Planning Program and (2) the Regional Medical Program, referred to on the Hill as the CHP and RMP amendments. Under the RMP amendment the Congress provided additional funding to large major hospitals if they would become the hub of healthcare information and services in a defined geographic area. The hospital was encouraged to apply NIH research information for distribution to the smaller rural hospitals and become the center for advanced medical care for the rural hospitals to feed into. They would provide advanced care in areas such as cancer treatment, cardiac care, and stroke. The RMP program led to development of specialty clinics across the country, including the Cleveland, Mayo, MD Anderson, and Lahey clinics.

The CHP program amendment required all Hill-Burton hospitals in the major metropolitan areas to form a CHP council and plan for the healthcare needs of their service area. If a metro area had 12 major hospitals, each with all the latest and expensive advanced medical equipment and each doing the same procedures, then a lot of duplication of services was taking place. The CHP program required those hospitals to form a council and discuss how best to plan and use the services while avoiding costly duplication. However, CHP was only advisory and there was no penalty if a group of hospitals failed to streamline and consolidate their services. The law only required hospitals to set up the process and meet and discuss how to better utilize services. In reality, while the hospitals recognized the high cost of duplicate equipment and the need for better planning and coordination, none were willing to give up their programs. If one hospital was to be the cancer center and another the heart center, the heart center would have to give up all its cancer revenue and likewise the cancer center of the hospital would have to give up its heart care revenues. Since there was no requirement and CHP was only advisory, hospitals and their boards were very reluctant to give up revenue and little realignment came out of the CHP program.

Summary

With Medicare and Medicaid in place, Congress set about determining how to properly staff the medical community to meet the needs of patients. Continuing to work in a spirit of bipartisan collaboration, it determined that there was a shortage of physicians, osteopathic doctors, and dentists. Passage of the Health Manpower Act and the Hill-Burton Act provided incentives for medical education and the construction of hospitals and other medical facilities. The result was an explosion in the number of medical specialists (encouraged by the areas of funding/study undertaken by the newly established National Institutes of Health), a lack of primary care physicians, and difficulty attracting medical professionals to rural areas. Amendments to Hill-Burton helped to address some of these issues, making it easier for hospitals to hire foreign-trained primary care physicians and providing incentives for rural areas to build facilities, hire physicians, and provide services to the poor. Conversely, in large cities where Hill-Burton funds were used for expansion, technology and services were being duplicated from hospital to hospital. Two additional amendments, the Comprehensive Health Planning Program and the Regional Medical Program, helped to consolidate regional services and led to the development of specialty clinics across the country.

References

Amendments to the Social Security Act, Pub. L. No. 92-603. 1972.

Health Professions Education Assistance Act, Pub. L. No. 88-128, 77 Stat 164. 1963.

Hill-Burton Act, Pub. L. No. 79-725, 60 Stat. 1040. 1946.

Immigration and Nationality Act, Pub. L. No. 89-236. 1965.

Medicare and Medicaid, Social Security Amendments, Pub. L. No. 80-97, 79 Stat 286. 1965.

Public Health Service Act, 42 U.S.C. 6A §201 et seq. 1944.

CHAPTER 4

The Cost Realities and Political Events' Impact on National Healthcare Action

Abstract In the 1970s, bipartisanship began to break down as disagreement about the role of government in healthcare increased. With both Medicare and Medicaid costs rising well beyond what were projected, some Democrats began to push for a national healthcare system, while Republicans argued for market-based cost containment. In 1972, more income tax dollars were spent on health and education than on defense, prompting President Nixon to take steps aimed at curbing healthcare expenditures. This included freezing appropriations for already-authorized healthcare programs under a continuing resolution. The Nixon administration referred to its approach to healthcare policy and the period of diminished funding as "new federalism," a philosophy of reducing federal support while moving administration and funding of healthcare programs to state and local governments. Congress passed the National Health Planning and Resources Development Act (NHPRDA) requiring any community or hospital that wished to build or expand a facility to first present evidence of need to the state health system agency. Congress also passed the Health Maintenance Organization Act (HMOA) encouraging local areas to develop an alternative to fee-for-service medical care by bringing together a comprehensive range of medical or healthcare services in a single organization.

Keywords President Nixon • Continuing resolution • New federalism • National Health Planning and Resources Development Act • Health Maintenance Organization Act • Budget and Impoundment Act

D. F. Lavanty, *Political Aspects of Health Care*,
https://doi.org/10.1057/978-1-137-40283-7_4

Lack of Data, Skyrocketing Costs

Between 1965 and 1972, changes in healthcare legislation continued to unfold. With Medicare and Medicaid providing reimbursement to the elderly and poor, the need for services was increasing and Congress was buoyed by the favorable public reaction to the Health Manpower Act and the revitalization of the Hill-Burton Act. Three trends were unfolding: (1) the concern of the tax writing committees upon realizing that the costs of the Medicare program had been miscalculated and it was becoming far costlier than projected, (2) the dysfunction within Congress with respect to tax writing and legislation committees enacting healthcare programs without regard for each other's legislative and policy goals, and (3) the legislative committees, having enacted the progressive infrastructure programs of Hill-Burton and Health Manpower Acts, started asking whether the time was right to move the US healthcare system in the direction of a national healthcare system.

The Medicare program, like Blue Cross, Blue Shield, and the for-profit insurance carriers, followed the insurance premise of *loss-based coverage for a medically necessary corrective condition* to activate reimbursement. Unlike modern coverage, which deals with preventive medicine and screening coverage for conditions like colorectal cancer, breast cancer, glaucoma, and diabetes, Medicare took the position there was only reimbursement for a *loss* (e.g. a diagnosed illness that needed correction). Wellness was not a factor to consider in early Medicare. Because preventive care such as early detection and intervention was not covered and therefore not utilized, a condition was typically diagnosed and identified as a medical necessity at or near the end stage, when it was most costly to treat. The healthcare actuarial experience had no risk data on end-stage medical conditions and their costs. The Senate Finance and House Ways and Means Committees were being briefed by the Department of Health and Human Services (HHS) that the cost of Medicare Part A was rising faster than projected.

By 1970 the two committees began to look at changes to the Medicare program to slow down rising costs. Senators Russell Long (D-LA), Herman Talmadge (D-GA) and House Ways and Means Committee Chairman Wilbur Mills (D-AK), along with two of the most knowledgeable and influential staff leaders of the period, Jay Constantine in the Senate and William Fullerton in the House, proposed two amendments designed to address the growth issue. One was to amend the US Criminal Code to enumerate specific healthcare actions that would be illegal. The most notable was the "anti-kickback" provision that made it a crime for a Medicare provider to receive remuneration from a supplier for specific referrals recommending a patient purchase their product. The committees were given data on such activities and how they increased costs. The second amendment was to require the medical societies in a state or major metropolitan area to establish a Professional Standards Review Organization (PSRO) to oversee utilization protocols and make recommendations to change medical standards when doing so would reduce reimbursement and establish cost containment as a national priority in future health policy legislation.

Legally, if a standard was agreed to by the PSRO, it became the legal standard to follow in malpractice cases. For example, one of the first tests administered to a Medicare patient who had a fall was a series of skull x-rays. The PSRO, under the guidance of medical experts (neurosurgeons and radiologists), determined the skull series provided no treatment benefit for a concussion or head injury and was therefore unnecessary. They recommended that the protocol be changed. The recommendation resulted in savings in the Medicare program in the form of less payments for head x-rays. These two amendments, while producing savings, were not getting at the core of the rising Medicare reimbursements—paying for the charges of procedures on a cost basis. It is important to note that Medicare Part A hospital coverage was patterned after Blue Shield, making payment based upon the hospital costs/consideration of cost reimbursement. This was changed in 1983 with legislation that adopted the reimbursement modality of Diagnosis-Related Groups (DRG), moving from cost-based reimbursement to prospective payment.

The Medicaid program was also far exceeding its projected costs. As adopted by each of the states, Medicaid was established to share the costs of healthcare services between federal and state tax revenues. One of the benefits that was causing concern was that many elderly persons were liquidating assets to be eligible for Medicaid (and therefore the long-term care provisions) by qualifying as living below the poverty level. During the early period of Medicare (1965–1972), elderly patients often required a lengthy hospital stay or even permanent long-term care after a high-cost medical procedure, care that they did not have the income to pay for. They would then be eligible for the state Medicaid long-term care program which would reimburse the nursing home for the cost of their care. Like reimbursement for the Medicare program, income eligibility for long-term care and its cost would also be addressed in 1983 to establish a means test and time frame for eligibility.

While the tax writing committees were reacting to the unanticipated growth and trying to counter it with legislative changes to the Federal Insurance Contributions Act (FICA) Medicare tax Part A coverage, the second trend in congressional dysfunction regarding healthcare policy became apparent with the enactment of infrastructure programs to complement the development of the national safety net of health insurance coverage. The complement was in the form of authorizing legislation developed by the Senate Health, Education, Labor and Pensions (HELP) Committee and the House Commerce Committee. The authorization and appropriation of funding for the infrastructure programs, together with funding for the National Institutes of Health (NIH) programs, resulted in the appropriation of the 1972 health and education portion of income tax dollars exceeding funding for defense spending that year, something that had never happened before. From 1965 to 1972, any bill regarding Medicare, healthcare infrastructure, and NIH authorization and appropriations that came up in the full House and Senate were overwhelmingly approved.

The resulting increase in Medicare costs (see Fig. 2.1 Annual Medicare Spending) and the large appropriation funding had members of Congress questioning whether they had gone too far, especially given global defense concerns regarding the Soviet Bloc, Cuba, and China and the need for greater defense spending. For its part, the House sought to establish a select task force to review the congressional roles of each committee with the goal of restructuring them to be more organized and efficient, and less costly. They requested that the task force pay attention to the roles of the committees in healthcare jurisdiction. The House reorganization plan, chaired by Richard Bolling (D-MO) presented to the full House a plan that would attempt to eliminate duplication, confusion, and dysfunction in healthcare policies and programs. The plan called for the House Ways and Means Committee (which up to this time had exclusive jurisdiction on Medicare and Medicaid) to have exclusive jurisdiction only over Medicare Part A and for the House Commerce Committee (who prior to the reorganization had no jurisdiction) to have exclusive jurisdiction over Medicaid and any bills or action dealing with Medicare Part B. Physician and other provider services—previously under the jurisdiction of the Ways and Means Committee for Medicare and Medicaid, and the Commerce Committee for public health programs such as Health Manpower and Hill-Burton would be jointly acted upon by both committees.

The result was a three-part process of the Senate Finance, House Ways and Means, and House Commerce Committees, each acting on healthcare legislation and policy. This action brought into focus for Congress the problems of Medicare cost increases, appropriation funding, and the need for some managers to be placed upon the healthcare system. Pragmatically, the reorganization plan would force Congress to coordinate healthcare policy between Medicare and the authorization programs. Philosophically, however, the time between 1969 and 1972 reinvigorated the national health debate, with one side favoring the status quo and advocating for greater marketplace involvement and the other favoring a move to a national health system like those in England and Canada.

However, since the politics of change were still positive, the 1972 Social Security Amendments (SSA) provided for Medicare eligibility for disabled individuals and adopted a national healthcare benefit covering renal care. These two additions were the capstone of the action period of 1965 to 1972 and were added notwithstanding the early concerns of the cost of the programs.

Programs in Need of Direction

While the reorganization was taking shape and Congress was focusing on the appropriation monies spent on healthcare, Senator Ted Kennedy (D-MA) and his allies put together a coalition of congressional liberals, labor leaders and other groups to form the "Committee of 100" who submitted draft legislation and held hearings on the issue of the United States developing a national health insurance system. They argued that a uniform healthcare system was the logical next step given that (1) funding was made available for the elderly and poor through Medicaid and Medicare, establishing health insurance as a bona fide condition of employment for major companies and (2) Congress authorized and appropriated funding for the Health Manpower Act (HMA) and Hill-Burton to expand the availability of both healthcare facilities and providers.

In January 1971, Senator Kennedy and Representative Martha Griffiths (D-AL) proposed the Kennedy-Griffiths Health Security Act containing the requirement that every health insurance program must offer cradle-to-grave coverage and a public program to cover the uninsured. Those members of the House and Senate who did not share Senator Kennedy's vision offered alternative legislative options. The House Ways and Means

Committee Chair, Rep. Al Ullman[1] (D-OR) authored legislation that would have all payments for healthcare be directed and managed by hospitals (similar to the German healthcare system). Representative Omar Burleson (D-TX), a member of the House Ways and Means Committee authored legislation that would have all health dollars and programs directed to the purchase of health insurance, and several other members authored legislation known as Medicredit that would provide tax deductions for those who purchased health insurance.

Each piece of proposed legislation reflected the member's relationship with his top constituencies; Senator Kennedy was promoting the labor movement agenda, Representative Ullman's plan supported hospitals, Representative Burleson's plan was supported by the health insurance industry and Medicredit was promoted by the American Medical Association (AMA). The last proposal put forward during the hearings and debate was legislation sponsored by Senators Russell Long and Abraham Ribicoff (D-CT) that would have federalized Medicaid, provided for children's healthcare (ultimately the Children's Health Insurance Program CHIP), and set up a catastrophic health insurance fund.

The debate over the direction of national healthcare started during the Nixon administration, which raised a discussion on offering an employer mandate as an alternative to expansion and continued into part of the Carter administration. No final action was taken on any of the programs, although, years later, President Carter liked the Long-Ribicoff approach and President Reagan supported congressional enactment of a catastrophic health plan. The catastrophic plan ran into a major problem with the elderly that will be discussed in later chapters.

With the debate over national health insurance and the many plans offered which highlighted the action period from 1965 to 1972 and raised considerable debate within Congress, the political compromise to avoid either proposed extreme (i.e. the Kennedy plan or the AMA Medicredit) was to advance those expansions, notwithstanding the additional costs. The costs of the additions, however, when balanced against the cost of a national health insurance program were extremely moderate and therefore politically acceptable and represented the last expansion until the 1980s.

[1] Ullman became Chair of the House Ways and Means Committee after Rep. Wilbur Mills in 1975. Mills retired from Congress in 1976, after public incidents with a stripper named Fanne Foxe came to light.

Reaction and Retraction

Concurrently with the proliferation of healthcare policy proposals, the Nixon administration began a reactive policy and political campaign against the expansion of Medicare and the funding of healthcare programs. As data showed growth in Medicare and appropriation spending on healthcare, conservative Democratic members of Congress, later known as "blue dog" Democrats, saw merit in some of President Nixon's proposals and were successful in freezing appropriations for the already-authorized healthcare programs. This action occurred in the legislative vehicle and is know as a "continuing resolution" and lasted from 1972 to 1982. In effect, healthcare appropriations were at the 1972 level for 10 years and, in some cases, even reduced.[2]

In terms of legislative process, a continuing resolution to fund the government can be no greater than the previous amount, but can be less. The Nixon administration referred to its approach to healthcare policy and the period of diminished funding as "new federalism," meaning that the administration supported the congressional funding reduction and at the same time promoted moving administration and funding of federal healthcare programs to state and local governments. States could apply the programs' aims (HMA, Hill-Burton, NIH) to the healthcare needs of their citizens rather than having decisions made at the federal level. Evidence of new federalism is seen in the amendments to Hill-Burton of Comprehensive Health Planning (CHP) and Regional Medical Program (RMP), referred to in the previous chapter as examples of the Democratic Congress adopting some of the Nixon administration's recommendations. The same was true in the HMA legislation when the emphasis was on primary care to address the needs of local communities to have healthcare providers. Further evidence of the Nixon approach to healthcare issues was the approval of funding for the Rand Corporation to conduct a study (the Rand Health Insurance Experiment) on the effects of cost-sharing on utilization of benefits. The study found a relationship between patient-borne costs and use of benefits. Utilization of benefits decreased when there was a higher cost to the patient and increased when the patient experienced greater savings.

[2] For additional information on continuing resolutions, see https://www.senate.gov/reference/resources/pdf/97-684.pdf, p. 13.

While the early years of the first Nixon administration were devoted to winding down the Vietnam War, there was also concern over the rising costs of healthcare and the cost of Medicare. The United States was in a recession when Nixon was elected, and these increases contributed to inflation that resulted in President Nixon imposing wage and price controls on the economy in August of 1971 under the authority given in the 1970 Economic Stabilization Act. Inflation had risen to 6% in 1970 and persisted at 4% from 1971 on. President Nixon issued a 90-day freeze on all wages and prices, which lasted for 1000 days. Inflation rates were even higher for healthcare costs and spending, resulting in a significant impact on healthcare policy in the Carter administration in 1977.

Upon his reelection in 1972, Nixon was determined to slow the economy and further reduce Congress' funding of domestic spending, particularly on healthcare. To do this, he refused to spend even the frozen amounts under the continuing resolution appropriated. This action by President Nixon ultimately led to the enactment in 1974 of the Budget and Impoundment Act, which required the president to have the approval of Congress when refusing to spend appropriated funds.

In effect, the Nixon administration ushered in an era of reaction and retraction to the aggressive period of healthcare legislation between 1965 and 1970. The administration was also successful in working with Congress on two other major health policy programs. Recognizing that the Hill-Burton amendment was not going to achieve the intended effect of limiting duplication and requiring coordinated planning, the administration proposed to Congress in 1974 a law requiring states to establish a program to set up a state health systems agency which would be responsible to grant certificates of needs (CONs) to hospitals to build or expand if the state wished to continue to receive federal Medicaid funding. The proposed National Health Planning and Resources Development Act (NHPRDA) would require that any community or hospital that wished to build or expand a facility to first present evidence of need to the state health system agency. Based on the evidence, the state agency would decide whether to grant the CON to build.

There was also a requirement that any hospital wanting to purchase capital equipment valued at more than $250,000 would be required to provide evidence of the need for the equipment. The intent was to prevent every hospital from purchasing the most expensive equipment. For example, the health systems agency might determine that if there was a

CT (computed tomography) scanner at one of the hospitals in the same geographical location, they would then look at population density to determine if there was a need for another CT scanner. If the health systems agency determined that one CT scanner was sufficient to handle the exam procedures for that population, they would deny a CON, requiring hospitals in the area to send patients needing a CT scan to the facility with the CT equipment. These measures would both help avoid duplication in the purchase of capital equipment and lower the rising costs of healthcare.

Immediately after the passage of the NHPRDA, Congress passed the Health Maintenance Organization Act (HMOA) in 1973. Under the law, local areas would be encouraged to have business, hospitals, labor, and healthcare practitioners form a nonprofit entity to explore if an HMO could be an alternative to fee-for-service medical care by bringing together a comprehensive range of medical or healthcare services in a single organization. If such a group was formed, federal funding would be available for a feasibility study to determine if the HMO model should be considered. Once HHS was convinced by the local nonprofit that the area could support the HMO concept, additional funding would be provided to implement an HMO. In the implementation phase the nonprofit would assess if the HMO should be a free-standing facility, like Kaiser Permanente or a network system such as a Preferred Provider Organization (PPO) with negotiated rates. The final stage was to provide federal funding to the nonprofit to market the HMO to the business community and seek their support to offer their employees the option to join the HMO. The imprint of Nixon's new federalism is seen in both the NHPRDA and the HMOA via their efforts to redirect healthcare programs to the local and state levels. NHPRDA was very successful and adopted by all the states. The HMOA took many more years to become accepted by the healthcare delivery system.

While these developments were being pursued by the Nixon administration and considered by Congress, President Nixon and his administration became embroiled in the Watergate scandal that began in June 1972 and ultimately ended with Nixon's resignation on August 8, 1974. Vice President Gerald Ford's first act as president was to pardon Nixon, which led to complete deadlock in Congress, causing the implementation of healthcare policy changes and other new federalism initiatives to be derailed until after the 1976 elections.

Summary

Here we see a lot of important developments that have had a lasting impact on the politics of federal health policy and health reform. We also begin to see breakdown in bipartisanship as well as disagreement about the role of government in healthcare. With both Medicare and Medicaid costs rising well beyond what were projected, some Democrats began to push for a national healthcare system, while Republicans argued for market-based cost containment. In 1972, more income tax dollars were spent on health and education than on defense, prompting President Nixon to take a number of steps aimed at curbing healthcare expenditures. This included freezing appropriations for already-authorized healthcare programs under a continuing resolution. The Nixon administration referred to its approach to healthcare policy and the period of diminished funding as "new federalism," a philosophy of reducing federal support while moving administration and funding of healthcare programs to state and local governments. In an effort to further stem rising costs and curb the growing trend of duplication in local services and in the purchase of capital equipment, Congress passed the National Health Planning and Resources Development Act (NHPRDA) requiring any community or hospital that wished to build or expand a facility to first present evidence of the need to the state health system agency. Shortly thereafter, Congress passed the Health Maintenance Organization Act (HMOA), encouraging local areas to develop an alternative to fee-for-service medical care by bringing together a comprehensive range of medical or healthcare services in a single organization.

References

Amendments to the Social Security Act, Pub. L. No. 92-603. 1972.

Budget and Impoundment Act, Pub. L. No. 93-344. 1974.

Children's Health Insurance Program Reauthorization Act, Pub. L. No. 111-3. 2009.

Federal Insurance Contribution Act, 26 U.S.C. §3101 et seq. 1972.

Health Maintenance Organization Act, 42 U.S.C. 6A §300e. 1973.

Health Professions Education Assistance Act, Pub. L. No. 88-128, 77 Stat. 164. 1963.

Hill-Burton Act, Pub. L. No. 79-725, 60 Stat. 1040. 1946.

Medicare and Medicaid, Social Security Amendments, Pub. L. No. 80-97, 79 Stat 286. 1965.

Multiple Authors. 1976. *Rand Health Insurance Experiment*. Source: Rand Corporation. https://www.rand.org/health/projects/hie.html. Accessed on July 11, 2018.

National Health Planning and Resources Development Act, Pub. L. No. 93-641. 1975.

U.S. Criminal Code, 18 U.S.C. §287. 1948.

CHAPTER 5

The Era of Budget Politics

Abstract The Carter administration provides a short but fraught lesson on the pitfalls of legislating on the emerging healthcare industry. Early in his administration, President Carter fashioned a plan of cost containment specifically for the healthcare industry. Dissension within the Democratic Party over how to sustainably move forward with both healthcare services and cost reductions significantly hindered Carter's initiatives. In addition, the various healthcare lobbies had become very effective, with contacts in every congressional district and political action committees contributing to congressional campaigns. The strength of these lobbies and their differing opinions on healthcare legislation effectively stalled Carter's efforts at cost containment and no major healthcare proposals were enacted during his administration. The development, purchase, and use of the sophisticated diagnostic technology also led to increases in the cost of medical care, as well as an increase in the number of malpractice suits and claims. The 1979 Iran hostage crisis provided the final nail in the Carter administration's coffin as all actions taken by Congress and the administration were directed toward resolving the hostage crisis.

Keywords President Carter • Cost containment • Technology • Iran hostage crisis • Standard of care

D. F. Lavanty, *Political Aspects of Health Care*,
https://doi.org/10.1057/978-1-137-40283-7_5

Carter's Attempt at Cost Containment

The political deadlock of the Watergate era ended with the election of Jimmy Carter, the former conservative Democratic Governor of Georgia, and with it the need to contain rising healthcare costs became a major priority for Democratic conservatives in Congress. President Carter indicated early on that addressing economic inflation would be a major focus of his administration. He planned to deal with rising healthcare costs by introducing legislative changes to Congress that would come to be known as a cost containment healthcare policy. The president and his advisors in healthcare focused on data the Nixon administration had developed during the wage and price program to deal with inflation and found the most aggressive inflation rate was in healthcare, with some data showing the healthcare rate of the gross domestic product (GDP) was 8%, which Carter believed was unsustainable. For what it's worth, in 2018, healthcare spending comprises nearly 18% of GDP and is deemed unsustainable (see Fig. 1.1).

The Carter administration took the economic position that capitalism would stabilize wages and prices in the general economy through supply, demand, and competition. However, healthcare costs were viewed as being locked in through health insurance and government programs and therefore outside of the competitive environment. The policy, therefore, would be to fashion a plan of cost containment specifically for the healthcare industry based upon the ideas that are applied to utilities (gas, electric, water, etc.) costs by state regulators, and that healthcare charges and increases would be subject to a similar process that state-regulated utilities underwent. The industry would have to provide documentation of rising costs to justify price increases. National standards would be applied to healthcare costs and increases.

The original idea of cost containment would have healthcare costs limited to an 11% increase and set up a mechanism for national data to be developed to determine future allowable increases. Once presented to Congress, cost containment legislation was developed by the House Ways and Means Committee and was being readied for consideration by the full House, but was not considered in the first session of the 95th Congress in 1977. Between the end of the first session and beginning of the second in January 1978, lobbying by the healthcare industry was nonstop and it was able to convince the House Ways and Means Committee to wait on bringing the legislation to the full House. At this period in healthcare advocacy, every healthcare organization had an effective lobbying arm in place with a strong program of key contacts in every congressional district, and most had political action committees contributing to Congress members' election committees. Very often, the various healthcare associations would have different views on healthcare legislation, but they were unified in their opposition to Carter's cost containment proposal. This was a formidable political base, including the American Medical Association (AMA), all the medical specialty societies, dentistry, allied health groups, hospital associations, and medical device manufactures.

A House Divided Makes Little Progress

Not having been successful in the cost containment legislation and still fostering an agenda to adopt some form of healthcare legislation, the Carter administration began to work with congressional sources to adopt an incremental approach to slow down cost increases, expand care where needed, and alter the delivery system by supporting the Health Planning and Resources Development Act (HPRDA) and Health Maintenance Organization Act (HMOA) enacted during the Nixon administration. The Carter administration adopted the elements of the Long-Ribicoff health insurance bill as a framework for some of the changes. They proposed legislation to Congress that would federalize the Medicaid program to develop a universal healthcare plan for children and look to add meaningful cost controls on hospital and other services.

This approach had mixed support. The more conservative Democrats and a block of Republican members were willing to support this approach, but it was not as well received by the liberal Democrats as the universal coverage healthcare program Carter promoted when running for office. Senator Ted Kennedy (D-MA) and Representative James Corman (D-CA) and their co-sponsors in the House and Senate had hoped Carter would support comprehensive reform for universal healthcare along the lines of the legislation they had previously introduced. They were so disappointed in the Carter administration's approach to national health reform that Senator Kennedy campaigned against the incumbent President Carter to be the Democratic nominee for president in the 1980 elections. The decision of Senator Kennedy to challenge a sitting president of his own party provides a textbook example to understanding the depth of the political importance of healthcare policy and the direction of the many competing philosophies at that time, and sets a preview of future efforts, like the Clinton reform, that do not have party agreement.

Carter's limited approach proposal did not attract a majority in the second session of the 95th Congress and no major healthcare proposals were enacted. With the Democratic congressional delegation sharply divided about the direction Congress should take on healthcare changes and policies to slow rapidly escalating costs, the last two years of the Carter administration (1978–1980) produced little in the way of major healthcare changes. During this period several Republican House members began to align with conservative Democrats regarding concerns over rising healthcare costs and its contributions to the federal deficit with costs nearing 12–13% of the gross domestic product (GDP). One Republican member of the House, David Stockman (R-MI), taking a page from the Carter approach to healthcare cost containment of controls, said in several committee settings that healthcare, rather than being treated as a utility, should become competitive and that Congress needed to find ways to introduce real marketplace competition into the healthcare system. Stockman, who later would become the Director of the Office of Management and Budget (OMB) under President Reagan, was issuing the healthcare community a warning shot in 1979.

But it was the events of November 4, 1979, that really slowed Congress down, preventing any real policy action on behalf of the Carter administration. On that date, students supporting the Iranian revolution took control of the US Embassy in Iran and held 52 Americans hostage for 444 days. As a result, all actions taken by Congress and the administration were directed toward the hostage crisis, and Congress otherwise functioned as a caretaker to keep the government going. This caretaker mentality was further heightened when Operation Eagle Claw, the administration's attempt to free the hostages, collapsed and every congressional office was overwhelmed with resolving the issue of how to get the hostages free. Ultimately, the hostage crisis would lead to Carter's defeat by Ronald Reagan in the 1980 presidential election.

Technology Throws Another Wrench in the Works

Increasing inflation, rising healthcare costs, escalating levels of authorized healthcare spending and Medicare and Medicaid far exceeding their projected costs all contributed to the rapid growth in healthcare costs. But there were also other forces at work. The expenses associated with modern medical technology were one more factor for policymakers to consider when assessing the increases in healthcare costs between 1965 and 1980.

President Nixon had proposed to Congress that funds for space exploration be limited to the development of a shuttle and not to further exploration of deep space. This decision had a negative impact on companies involved from 1960 on in the development of the propulsion technology needed to send rockets into outer space, as well as the telemetric information to maintain communication with astronauts and to monitor data on a trip to the moon. Many of the companies that had been involved in the space race began to develop healthcare equipment and provided the telemetric data for use and application to healthcare industry.

The computed tomography (CT) scan, the 20-channel blood analyzer, and the fetal monitor, to name a few, demonstrate a direct connection between the technology of space and healthcare. One member of Congress, Representative Olin Teague (D-TX), Chairman of the House Science Committee was the author of legislation to track the impact of space-age technology on all aspects of American product development. The Technology Assessment Act of 1972 authorized and funded the development of the Office of Technology Assessment (OTA) to provide Congress with objective and authoritative analysis of complex scientific and technical issues and developments. In 1978, at the request of several congressional committees, OTA undertook a study to determine the cost-effectiveness of medical technology, bringing the CT scanner to the attention of Congress as one more expensive item contributing to increased healthcare costs. CT scanners cost approximately $1.2 million each and, if just one-third of the new Hill-Burton hospitals purchased a new CT scanner using cost reimbursement and the allowable capital equipment purchase provision under Medicare, the cost would be extreme. Furthermore, the cost would be paid out of Medicare reimbursement and to a lesser extent, third-party private insurance.

The action of the purchase and use of the sophisticated technology also led to increases in the cost of medical malpractice insurance to cover the cost of an increase in the number of malpractice suits and claims. In a malpractice case, an expert physician is called upon to present the community standard in evidence to the jury to consider whether the defendant violated the standard. The standard is the result of the agreed-upon care to be provided in an area for each medical procedure. When the high-tech instrumentation of the CT scanner or 20-channel blood analyzer is added to the defined standard of care, a physician who chooses not to utilize them when treating a patient that the technology could benefit will be found negligent and the suing patient awarded damages.

Initially, these types of cases resulted in increased premiums to protect the practitioner and practitioners raised their charges to cover those increases. As the use of technology became the recognized standard of care, healthcare practitioners, to avoid any exposure to malpractice, practiced defensive medicine, ordering batteries of cutting-edge technology tests as a matter of course, and the impact of defensive medicine established additional testing costs, many of which might not be called for in the diagnosis. Regarding the 20-channel blood analyzer, studies showed many ordered tests were unnecessary or duplicative and the reimbursement for those tests were reduced in a patient's blood panel or profile.

A Political Process in Chaos

The impact of the increasing costs of Medicare and Medicaid, federal tax dollars expended on health manpower education, hospital construction, disease prevention, and the impact of technology in this period cannot be stressed enough. There was a rising level of concern among federal policymakers—Congress, their professional staff, and members of the Department of Health and Human Services—that to be able to act and address these issues, a unified political process had to be aligned. Faced with healthcare cost increases and the need for legislative action to address them, the political process was at war with itself. First, in the era of Richard Nixon, due to the discovery of a break-in at the Watergate offices of the Democratic National Committee, the Democrats in Congress sought to impeach Nixon and hosted endless committee hearings which engendered extreme discord between the competing political parties. Second, Carter's election produced a struggle among Democrats regarding healthcare policy, while Democrats and the electorate struggled with the Iran hostage crisis. And third, discord between the Democratic president and Democratic senators over the direction of healthcare policy all contributed to an environment where it was impossible to achieve a political unification of purpose to deal with healthcare issues.

With the election of President Reagan in 1980, a Republican Senate and a Democratic House, the comity of purpose in the balance of domestic and defense spending was achieved and the healthcare reformation began, moving healthcare from an era of government administration to one of government management.

Summary

The Carter administration provides a short but fraught lesson on the pitfalls of legislating the emerging healthcare industry. Early in his administration, President Carter fashioned a plan of cost containment specifically for the healthcare industry. Dissension within the Democratic Party over how to sustainably move forward with both healthcare services and cost reductions significantly hindered Carter's initiatives. In addition, the various healthcare lobbies had become very effective, with contacts in every congressional district and political action committees contributing to Congressional campaigns. The strength of these lobbies and their differing opinions on healthcare legislation effectively stalled Carter's efforts at cost containment and no major healthcare proposals were enacted during his administration. The development, purchase, and use of sophisticated diagnostic technology also led to increases in the cost of medical care, as well as an increase in the number of malpractice suits and claims. The 1979 Iran hostage crisis provided the final nail in the Carter administration's coffin, as all actions taken by Congress and the administration were directed toward resolving the hostage crisis. In the next chapter, we will see how the election of Republican President Reagan in 1980 ushered in a new era of healthcare reform, moving from an era of government administration to one of government management.

References

Amendments to the Social Security Act, Pub. L. No. 92-603. 1972.

Health Maintenance Organization Act, 42 U.S.C. 6A §300e. 1973.

Health Professions Education Assistance Act, Pub. L. No. 88-128, 77 Stat. 164. 1963.

Hill-Burton Act, Pub. L. No. 79-725, 60 Stat. 1040. 1946.

Medicare and Medicaid, Social Security Amendments, Pub. L. No. 80-97, 79 Stat 286. 1965.

Multiple Authors. 1978. *Assessing the Efficacy and Safety of Medical Technologies.* U.S. Congress Office of Technology Assessment. Source: Office of Technology Assessment. http://ota.fas.org/reports/7805.pdf. Accessed on July 11, 2018.

National Health Planning and Resources Development Act, Pub. L. No. 93-641. 1975.

CHAPTER 6

The Reagan Era of Politics and Healthcare

Abstract Bipartisanship made a resurgence during the Reagan administration with the president and Speaker of the House Tip O'Neill (D-MA) setting the tone. Together, under budget reconciliation procedures, Congress was able to both obtain reductions in healthcare spending and maintain most Medicare and Medicaid benefits by applying the reduction in reimbursements to payments to hospitals, healthcare providers, and suppliers under an omnibus reconciliation bill. Congress made a serious misstep in passing the 1988 Medicare Catastrophic Coverage Act, which raised premiums on seniors while providing them with little benefit in return and elicited outrage from the electorate and lobbying groups. It was repealed a little over a year later. There was a boom in the number of women elected to Congress and they were successful in passing legislation to improve the accuracy of screening tests for cervical and breast cancer—issues that had received little attention in the past. This led to a major shift from Medicare only reimbursing for covered medical conditions to reimbursing for screening tests. Continuing its efforts to cut costs, the Congress adopted fee schedules to regulate the amount spent on some equipment and procedures and required physicians to participate in Medicare if they wished to receive future payment updates.

Keywords President Reagan • Budget reconciliation • Medicare Catastrophic Coverage Act • Women • Diagnosis-Related Groups • Omnibus Budget Reconciliation Act

D. F. Lavanty, *Political Aspects of Health Care*,
https://doi.org/10.1057/978-1-137-40283-7_6

The Budget Reconciliation Process

With the aftermath of the Watergate scandal and the Iran hostage crisis behind the nation, the divided Congress and the Reagan administration engaged in eight years of major changes in Medicare, Medicaid, and public health service programs spending. These changes were brought about by the personal comity established between President Reagan and the Speaker of the House, Thomas "Tip" O'Neill (D-MA). It is well documented by those who worked both in the administration and for the Speaker that the two leaders had an amiable working relationship. While each came from divergent political views, there was an underlying belief in each other's positions and a willingness to work toward acceptable compromises. Nevertheless, the two men had their disagreements. David Stockman, director of the Office of Management and Budget (OMB), directed the Reagan administration to reduce the influence of government in healthcare and move the system to more market-based forces, while Speaker O'Neill and House Democrats insisted that Medicare and Medicaid benefits and services not be reduced. As it turned out, they were able to do both under a process known as budget reconciliation.

Before continuing to discuss each of the healthcare changes, it is important that the process of budget reconciliation be understood. When the House and Senate finally agree on budget bills, three things happen: (1) the agreement sets the spending limits for each federal category, (2) it is binding only on Congress, and (3) no action is required from the president. For example, the budget agreement could provide $250 billion for Medicare spending with $30 billion in savings and $245 billion in defense spending. The next step in the process is for the congressional committees with jurisdiction (for Medicare and Medicaid: the House Ways and Means and Commerce and Senate Finance; for defense spending: the House and Senate Armed Services Committees) to enact legislation following the budget agreement. Upon enactment, the legislation is sent to the president for his signature. Under the Congressional Budget and Impoundment Act, if the congressional committees with jurisdiction have not enacted legislation to reach the congressionally adopted budget resolution within the budget cycle then the budget process calls for the Budget Committee to send to each legislative committee reconciliation instructions whereby each committee with jurisdiction submits to the budget committee their legislative changes. The budget committee then presents to each body of Congress a budget reconciliation bill to be voted on (containing all the changes of each committee) and sent to the president for signature. This is where the terms Omnibus Budget Reconciliation Act (OBRA) and Consolidated Omnibus Budget Reconciliation Act (COBRA) come from. A budget reconciliation bill passed by Congress and sent to the president must be signed or vetoed by the president *in whole* as the president does not have line item veto authority.

One other procedural rule of note in the budget process is the Byrd Rule, named after Senator Robert Byrd (D-WV). Under the Byrd Rule, the Senate needs only a simple majority to pass a reconciliation bill (no filibuster). The rule further prohibits (1) passage of legislation that would significantly increase the deficit beyond a ten-year term and (2) inclusion of extraneous provisions that aren't directly related to meeting the budget targets. This amendment to the Congressional Budget Act of 1974 will come to play an important role in future actions on healthcare.

At the same time, a perfect storm of political circumstances developed that would lead to changes in healthcare. First, President Reagan campaigned on reducing taxes, dedicating most federal resources to defense, and reducing domestic spending. Second, the Budget and Impoundment Control Act of 1974 (BICA) that required a president to get congressional approval to refrain from spending appropriated funds also created a congressional mechanism to address the nation's resources and spending. Under BICA, Congress was required to set up House and Senate budget committees to determine congressional spending levels for each Congress and set up the Congressional Budget Office (CBO) to provide the information upon which to determine spending and the cost of legislation.

By 1980, the budget process of each congressional committee and the OMB was fully operational and provided Congress with a completed American chart of accounts[1] resulting in a finding that the 1980 tax cuts established a 100 billion deficit and by 1982 the deficit grew to $270 billion. Finally, President Reagan put together a commission to study the fiscal integrity of the Social Security and Medicare Federal Insurance Contributions Act (FICA) Trust Funds. The commission reported in June 1982 that, given the rate of FICA contributions and spending on Social Security and Medicare, the trust funds would run out of money by 2001. In December 1982, the commission further reported that, at the current rate of FICA funds dedicated to Medicare and the rate of expenditure, the

[1] A chart of accounts organizes the finances of a government or other entity by segregating expenditures, revenue, assets, and liabilities.

Medicare portion of the fund would run out by 1987. These three circumstances led to 10 years of continuous legislative enactments that changed the direction of the healthcare system by reducing Medicare and Medicaid. During that same time, however, eligibility standards were expanded, notwithstanding the drastically limiting domestic funding for healthcare infrastructure programs. In the final analysis, predictions of Medicare going broke changed the politics of reconciliation and healthcare policymaking.

The ten-year process of change in healthcare legislation was helped along by the invocation of the budget reconciliation process and the underlying good will of the president and Speaker. In negotiations on budget reconciliation, the administration was able to obtain reductions in healthcare spending and Congress was able to maintain most benefits by applying the reduction in reimbursements to payments to hospitals, physicians, and other healthcare providers and suppliers, thus embedding all those changes in one omnibus reconciliation bill without having to bring each issue up under separate bills. The political reality for members of Congress who may have been lobbied by healthcare associations to resist the reductions was to advise the associations that they did not agree with the cuts, but there were so many other issues in the omnibus bill they supported that they had to vote for it. An astute healthcare association lobbying Congress during this period would have recognized reductions were coming and advised their associations to prepare for the changes while attempting to find the best way to work with Congress to lessen the impact of the reductions.

Further complicating the budget reconciliation process was a 1985 amendment to the budget legislation referred to as the Gramm–Rudman–Hollings Balanced Budget and Emergency Deficit Control Act that required legislation be enacted to make reductions in federal spending that would bring the deficit to zero over a period of five years—it was later changed to add an additional five years because of legal issues.

The reconciliation process began in earnest in 1980–1981 with the 1981 OBRA which provided specific increases in defense spending, a framework for a national tax cut and a reduction in domestic spending. This limited funding for the Health Manpower Act and Hill-Burton programs. The next move was the Tax Equity and Fiscal Responsibility Act (informally referred to as "the Reagan tax cut") of 1982 as a follow-up to the budget act. The law provided for across-the-board tax cuts, but in payment for those cuts, as determined by CBO savings, changes were made to the Medicare and Medicaid programs but also included some tax increases to stem the tide of red ink. For Medicare, the process of revenue sharing between hospitals and hospital-based physicians was prohibited. The provision would generate savings on paper, as determined in the budget process and would help offset the loss of revenue from the tax cuts.

Another amendment that would generate savings and have a major impact required that states, in order to be eligible for their Medicaid payments, change their Medicaid programs to become "prudent purchasers" of healthcare services. Each state would have to demonstrate its adoption of a cost-saving program. For example, a state might develop a program of competitive bidding for lab or other services. The state of New Jersey adopted a program studied at Yale, which called for payment of Medicaid hospital services on a prospective payment system through Diagnostic Related Groups (DRGs). DRGs divided diagnoses based on affected body systems (determined by the Yale study) and categorized hospitalization costs based on these diagnoses to determine how much to pay for a patient's hospital stay. Rather than paying the hospital for what it spent caring for a hospitalized patient, the program paid the hospital a fixed amount based on the patient's DRG. If the hospital spent less than the DRG payment while treating the patient, it made a profit, if it spent more, it sustained a loss. The study showed that within each major illness (e.g. a heart attack) there were several causes and once the diagnosis determined the exact cause, it would be matched with a predetermined payment which is all the hospital would be reimbursed. Gone was cost-based reimbursement. This system would receive major refinements by the HCFA, now the Centers for Medicare and Medicaid Services (CMS) when Congress enacted the Social Security Reform act of 1983 requiring that all reimbursement for Medicare patients be based upon the prospective payment system of DRGs.

Because the Social Security Commission report of December 1982 indicated that the Medicare Trust Fund would be insolvent by 1987, Congress, with little opposition from its members and in spite of great opposition from the hospital community, passed an amendment to the Medicare program requiring all reimbursement to hospitals be on a prospective payment system based upon the DRGs by 1986. According to the CBO analysis, this provision would produce enough savings to preserve the trust fund until 2000.

Throughout these discussions, leaders of both parties echoed the tone set by the president and Speaker of the House. Pete Stark (D-CA),

Chairman of the House Ways and Means Subcommittee on Health, never hesitated to work with the ranking Republican, William Gradison (R-OH), and they jointly agreed that the DRG payment system was necessary. Stark indicated in the hearings on the legislation that members of Congress were the trustees of the Medicare program and given the Social Security Commission report, they had no alternative but to act to save the program and Gradison agreed.

In 1985, the budget process became even more important with the addition of the Gramm–Rudman–Hollings Balanced Budget and Emergency Deficit Control Act requiring reductions to remove the deficit by the early 1990s. The 1985–1986 budget bill is referred to as COBRA and is known for its provision requiring employers to allow employees who lose their jobs to be able to continue enrollment in their health insurance. It also contained healthcare provisions regarding Medicare secondary payer requirements. For example, if a patient had private insurance, the private carrier would be billed first, and Medicare billing would be delayed. The CBO scored this as a savings provision. Further, COBRA required the Medicaid programs for long-term care and nursing home care payment formula for eligibility be subject to a look-back provision allowing the state to go back three years to see if a recipient disposed of assets with the intent of becoming eligible for long-term care.

Good Intentions Meet Catastrophe

The Reagan administration also saw an amazing example of how well-intended federal healthcare policies can run afoul of the electorate. After much discussion within the administration, President Reagan, at the strong urging of the Secretary of Health and Human Services (HHS), Dr. Otis Bowen, recommended Congress enact a catastrophic health insurance plan which would (1) eliminate all in-patient deductibles after reaching the hospital in-patient cap, (2) set up a payment level under Part B that if exceeded would be covered by the plan, and (3) set a threshold on prescription drug payments. The program would be funded by increases in Medicare premiums—an increase of $4.92 per month on top of the then $17.90 Medicare monthly premium. Even though the legislation was well received in Congress, several members, including Senator Claude Pepper (D-FL), a longtime advocate for senior healthcare, were concerned that, for the price seniors would be required to pay, the coverage did not get at the major costs of long-term care or prescription drugs.

In June 1988, the House passed the Medicare Catastrophic Coverage Act. When the American Association of Retired Persons (AARP), the Committee to Save Medicare, and other senior advocacy groups saw that the additional premium would be much higher with no benefit coverage for long-term care and prescription drugs, they lobbied Congress to amend or repeal the legislation. The pharmaceutical lobby, which supported the repeal of the Catastrophic Coverage Act because it allowed the regulation of prices by the government, will later play a role in President Bush's Medicare Modernization Act, resulting in another prohibition of the government negotiating prescription drug prices. It was well publicized that the Chairman of the House Ways and Means Committee, Dan Rostenkowski (D-IL) was at a meeting in his district when an elderly woman chased him down and demanded the legislation be repealed. Elderly people across the country made the same arguments to their members of Congress. In November 1989, by a vote of 360-66 the Medicare Catastrophic Coverage Act was repealed. As President Clinton would learn later, when you propose major changes in healthcare that impact the everyday electorate, it's important to make sure they support it, even if it appears to be good policy to Congress.

Women's Voices Amplified

Another political shift was taking place during the 1980s as well. More women were being elected to state legislatures, governors' offices, and both houses of Congress. At the congressional level, not only were women legislators increasing in numbers but also in power. During the 1980s, Congress saw the emergence of women leaders such as Rep. Geraldine Ferraro (D-NY), Rep. Lindy Boggs (D-LA), Sen. Olympia Snowe (R-ME), Sen. Barbara Boxer (R-CA), Mary Rose Oakar (D-OH), Rep. Barbara Kennelly (D-CA), and Sen. Barbara Mikulski (D-MD). With the increase in numbers and power, women became a political bloc demanding consideration of issues they supported.

During this time, two issues surfaced highlighting the need to address women's unique healthcare issues and planting a seed for future political and policy changes. The first involved errors in the Papanicolaou test (pap test) to screen for cervical cancer. Error data showed that several women had died from cervical cancer because of missed findings in the pap test. When the errors received media coverage, women legislators and their aides demanded action, noting how long women's healthcare issues had gone unaddressed. This led to the enactment of the Clinical Laboratory Improvement Amendments or (CLIA) in 1988. The law required all laboratories to have a certificate issued by an agency of the Department of Health and Human Services (HHS) to perform lab tests. Labs were required to implement quality control measures and pass a proficiency test in order to receive HHS certification.

The other women's health issue that came forward in this period was mammography screening for breast cancer. The American Cancer Society (ACS) and the National Cancer Institute developed data indicating that the number one cause of death for women was breast cancer. The ACA worked with the American College of Radiology (ACR) to develop criteria facilities that must be met to perform mammography screening. Upon the insistence of Representative Mary Rose Oakar (D-OH), hearings were held on mammogram procedures and the criteria for ensuring quality breast cancer screening. Senator Barbara Mikulski (D-MD) insisted on an amendment in the 1987 reconciliation bill to provide coverage for mammography screening and to require the Health Care Finance Administration (HCFA) to develop quality standards based upon the recommendations of the ACS and the accreditation program of the ACR. These amendments applied only to screening for Medicare patients.

In 1994, Congress expanded the criteria for all mammography screenings and passed the Mammography Quality Standards Act requiring any entity doing screenings to be accredited by the Federal Drug Administration (FDA). By addressing the two issues of ensuring quality testing, Congress entered the realm of quality control and set the stage for Medicare and Medicaid to begin reimbursing for screening services. This would be a major shift from only reimbursing for covered medical conditions to reimbursing for screening tests, which outcome studies had demonstrated could reduce costs in later life. By 1997, Medicare was reimbursing for all major screening tests.

Making Fees and Reimbursements Meaningful

The 1987–1988 budget reconciliation not only had to merge all Medicare and Medicaid changes into one omnibus bill but because the Gramm–Rudman–Hollings Balanced Budget and Emergency Deficit Control Act (hereafter the Gramm–Rudman–Hollings Act) required reductions to zero out the deficit, Medicare and Medicaid had to make further reimbursement cuts. The legislation enacted fee schedules for clinical laboratory services and durable medical equipment, reducing payment by 40% and eventually moving, in some cases, to competitive bidding. The laboratory community promised to support the reductions if the law would also remove the requirement of collecting co-pays from patients. They felt that removing the administrative costs of the collecting co pays would come close to making up for payment reductions for the tests.

Another example of a healthcare association working with Congress was the ACR's recommendation that a fee schedule be developed that would result in reductions of payments for radiology services, with the method of how those reductions were to occur being determined by the HCFA working with them on the reduction formula. In 1987, Congress was also considering implementing a plan supported by the AMA to redesign Medicare reimbursements to physicians based upon a study from the Harvard School of Public Health under the direction of economist Dr. William Hsiao. The Hsiao study developed the Resource-Based Relative Value Scale (RBRVS), which assigned relative values to the different procedures performed by primary care providers or other medical providers. The study had the premise of determining which physicians provided the most service to Medicare patients based upon the physician's time with the patient and the intensity of the visit. The study referred to this process as *cognitive care.* Investigators found that because primary care physicians spent more time in cognitive care and procedurals with patients than other practitioners, and because surgeons spent less time with patients, there should be a realignment of fees for procedurals and surgeons and increased fees for practitioners providing cognitive care.

Radiologists, seeing this, knew their reimbursement for computed tomography (CT) scans and Magnetic Resonance Imaging (MRI) scans would see significant reductions under the proposal if enacted by Congress, so they requested that Congress authorize radiologists, pathologists, and surgeons to develop a meaningful fee schedule. Congress authorized in the 1987 budget reconciliation legislation the authority for the HCFA to work with the specialists on how these realignments would occur. Radiologists and surgeons spent two years working with HCFA and, when the RBRVS was finally enacted in 1989 as part of OBRA, reimbursements were reduced; however, the reductions were moderated pursuant to the agreed-upon formula under the fee schedule.

The other provision that was added in the 1987 budget bill was the physician participating and nonparticipating provisions of Medicare. If a provider agreed to take what Medicare would pay without charging the patient any additional fee, then, in subsequent years, those providers would get payment updates. If a provider did not agree to participate and take the assigned fee they would be limited to charging their patient the 1987 amount and would be prohibited from increasing their fees from then on. Prior to this, providers were allowed to increase their actual charges under Medicare every July, but under this provision charges would be frozen at the current rate unless providers agreed to participate.

Bipartisanship Upended by a Newt

In the 1988 election, George H. W. Bush, President Reagan's Vice President, was elected President. The Bush administration was committed to continuing the reimbursement reductions to providers under the reconciliation process. The 1989 budget reconciliation legislation provided additional reductions in hospital payments, including reductions in payments for the purchase of capital equipment. The bill also provided that, over the next several years, the Medicare program would adopt the RBRVS system for reimbursing practitioners and included further reductions in laboratory and medical equipment payments. The Reagan-Bush era in healthcare succeeded in restructuring the federal role in healthcare payment and programs, but the Democratic Congress was able to maintain the benefits provided under Medicare and Medicaid by shifting those reductions to the providers via budget reconciliation.

During the many reimbursement changes being made from 1980 to 1990, the political climate allowed for some interesting negotiations. Among them was what is referred to as the "Waxman Wedge". Every reconciliation bill for Medicare and Medicaid changes based upon the Legislative Reorganization Act of 1970 required three committees to agree on the changes: the Senate Finance Committee, the House Ways and Means Committee, and the House Commerce Committee. The House Commerce Committee had jurisdiction for Medicaid and the Chair of the Health Subcommittee, Henry Waxman (D-CA)—who was always appointed as a negotiator on Medicaid—would always find a way to expand and protect the Medicaid program while the many reductions were being made to Medicare. Waxman knew that it would be difficult for Republicans to oppose giving states the option to adopt policy changes to Medicaid. He made these changes more palatable by spreading the costs over time so that they were not alarmingly high. It is politically noteworthy that at a time of major reductions, Waxman was able to expand Medicaid eligibility and benefits from 1984 to 1990 based upon the poverty level of pregnant women, infants, and children. Everyone in the legislative process, both staffers and lobbyists, knew to get any final bill in reconciliation, Mr. Waxman's support was needed, and that his support came with getting those changes to Medicaid.

According to the Congressional Budget Office, between 1980 and 1990, Congress was able to reduce payments to Medicare and Medicaid providers enough to save $92 billion. Before leaving the 1980s and moving from the last two years of the Bush administration to the Clinton administration, one other event of note occurred that would shape the political landscape for decades. In 1987, after Representative O'Neill retired, Jim Wright (D-TX), was elected Speaker of the House and became the first Speaker to resign from Congress. Led by a House member from Georgia, Newt Gingrich (R-GA), an ethics investigation was conducted over the handling of funds by the Speaker from a book sale. Mr. Wright resigned based on the ethics issues. Democratic members of Congress blamed Gingrich, vowing privately to get "even" and since that event, there has been very little House congressional comity or bipartisan support on healthcare legislation, except for the 1997 Balanced Budget Act negotiated between the Republican Congress and Democratic President Clinton.

President George H. W. Bush served out his remaining two years dealing with the Persian Gulf War, anger over his pledge to not raise taxes and rising inflation—which led to the election of President Clinton who made healthcare a major issue in his election platform.

Summary

Bipartisanship made a resurgence during the Reagan administration with the president and Speaker of the House Tip O'Neill (D-MA) setting the tone. Together, under budget reconciliation procedures, Congress was able to both obtain reductions in healthcare spending and maintain most Medicare and Medicaid benefits by applying the reduction in reimbursements to payments to hospitals, healthcare providers, and suppliers under an omnibus reconciliation bill. Most of the changes made during the Reagan administration were well received by the electorate; however, Congress made a serious misstep in passing the 1988 Medicare Catastrophic Coverage Act, which raised premiums on seniors, while providing them with little benefit in return. It was repealed a little over a year later. During this time Congress saw a (relative) boom in the number of women elected in the House and Senate. The women legislators were successful in passing legislation to improve the accuracy of screening tests for cervical and breast cancer—issues that had received little attention in the past. This led to a major shift from Medicare only reimbursing for covered medical conditions to reimbursing for screening tests. Continuing efforts to cut costs, Congress adopted fee schedules to regulate the amount to be spent on some equipment and procedures and required physicians to participate in Medicare if they wished to receive future payment updates. Elected in 1988, President George H.W. Bush continued the reimbursement reductions to providers under the reconciliation process, and between 1980 and 1990, Congress was able to reduce payments to Medicare and Medicaid providers enough to save $92 billion.

References

Amendments to the Social Security Act, Pub. L. No. 98-21. 1983.

Balanced Budget Act, Pub. L. No. 105-33, 111 Stat 251. 1997.

Budget and Impoundment Act, Pub. L. No. 93-344. 1974.

Clinical Laboratory Improvement Amendments, Pub. L. No. 114-255. 1988.

Congressional Budget Office. 1989. *The Economic and Budget Outlook: 1990–1994.* Source: Congressional Budget Office. https://www.cbo.gov/sites/default/files/101st-congress-1989-1990/reports/89-cbo-032.pdf. Accessed on July 11, 2018.

Consolidated Omnibus Reconciliation Act, Pub. L. No. 99-272, 100 Stat 82. 1985.

Extraneous Matter in Reconciliation Legislation (Byrd Rule), 2 U.S.C. §644. 1985.

Federal Insurance Contribution Act, 26 U.S.C. §3101 et seq. 1972.

Gramm–Rudman–Hollings Balanced Budget and Emergency Deficit Control Act, Pub. L. No. 99-177. 1985.

Hill-Burton Act, Pub. L. No. 79-725, 60 Stat. 1040. 1946.

Legislative Reorganization Act, Pub. L. No. 91-510. 1970.

Mammography Quality Standards Act, Pub. L. No. 102-539. 1994.

Medicare Catastrophic Coverage Act. H.R. 2470. 1988.

Omnibus Budget Reconciliation Act, Pub. L. No. 97-35. 1981.

Rich, Spencer. 1987. *Reagan Backs 'Catastrophic' Protection for Aged, But Not the Bowen Plan.* Source: The Washington Post. https://www.washingtonpost.com/archive/politics/1987/01/28/reagan-backs-catastrophic-protection-for-aged-but-not-the-bowen-plan/633102d9-fe90-4875-8d08-da504ced4b16/?noredirect=on&utm_term=.96ad91cbb088. Accessed on July 11, 2018.

Tax Equity and Fiscal Responsibility Act of 1982, Pub. L. No. 97-248. 1982.

CHAPTER 7

Medicare Meets the Marketplace: The Bush-Clinton Years

Abstract Due to an economic downturn in the late 1980s and early 1990s, employers moved to adopt managed care plans which reduced costs but limited employee options. This era saw a period of reduced and managed benefits for employees and no coverage for those who were laid off. Democratic presidential candidate Bill Clinton put the issues of unemployment and healthcare on the national stage. Upon election, Clinton instituted a task force, headed by then-First Lady Hillary Clinton to develop a healthcare plan. Eschewing input from Congress and other stakeholders, the task force handpicked advisors and met in closed-door sessions, virtually guaranteeing opposition from all quarters. The negative national attention given the Clinton healthcare reform efforts resulted in political fallout during the 1994 midterm elections where control of both the House and the Senate went to the Republicans. In 1996, the Congress passed the Health Insurance Portability and Accountability Act (HIPAA), allowing employees to continue coverage when changing jobs. Additional progress was made near the end of the Clinton administration with the passage of the 1997 Balanced Budget Act, the enactment of Medicaid Part C, and the Children's Health Insurance Program (CHIP), providing health insurance to children of parents below a certain income threshold.

Keywords Managed care • Reengineering • Clinton Health Access Initiative • Health Insurance Portability and Accountability Act • Patient's Bill of Rights • Medicare Part C

D. F. Lavanty, *Political Aspects of Health Care*,
https://doi.org/10.1057/978-1-137-40283-7_7

The Move to Managed Care

While President George H. W. Bush had led the international task force to rebuke Saddam Hussein for the takeover of Kuwait in early 1991 and held a high approval rating from the American electorate, his advisors felt he had done enough to be in a good position for his reelection effort. However, the American economy was lagging in the late 1980s and early 1990s and many major American corporations jumped on the bandwagon of "reengineering"—a business concept applied by major corporations as they downsized operations and laid off employees—to put a positive spin on it, corporations would tell shareholders they were "reengineering" to overcome their losses from increased overhead and foreign competition.

Health insurance was a major source of increased overhead. Corporations saw increases in their healthcare plans go up by as much as 74%. In part, those increases were due to the cost shift by practitioners and hospitals. Because of the losses they sustained in the $92 billion in reductions under Medicare and Medicaid during the heyday of budget reconciliation, practitioners and hospitals altered their markets and protocols from just doing the major medical procedures under Medicare (i.e. hips, knees and cataracts) to increasing those services for patients in their 50s and 60s who were covered under private insurance through employer-sponsored plans. Because of this cost shift, corporations were demanding that health insurers find ways to deal with the cost increases. In response, in the late 1980s, the private health insurance market promoted healthcare plans that "managed" the care of the employee, which resulted in limits on benefits and services and less flexibility for the employee in choosing both providers and services. The change by employers to adopt managed care plans was met with great frustration among employee groups.

If the overhead could not be reduced in the new healthcare market, corporations would move to reengineer. When a company reengineered itself, it reduced employees through layoffs. Employees who were laid off lost their benefits, the primary one being health insurance. The era saw a period of reduced and managed benefits for the employees who remained and no coverage for those who were laid off. Companies were required to offer the laid off employees continued coverage under the Consolidated Omnibus Budget Reconciliation Act (COBRA), but employees had to pay the fees themselves, which was very expensive when unemployed.

The move to managed care set off a political storm in Congress to legislate, and by the mid-1990s, Congress wanted to enact laws regulating the process as a matter of national policy, determining that certain services *could not be limited by* health insurance companies. For example, the number of days a woman spends in the hospital after giving birth. Attempts to cut costs by reducing post-natal stays were referred to as "drive by deliveries." The Bush reelection advisers underestimated the impact of the economic slowdown, layoffs, overall corporate losses and the effect on the working class, especially in terms of lost benefits. An early sign of the effect the economy was having on the working middle class came in a special election in Pennsylvania following the death of Senator John Heinz (R-PA) in an airplane crash on April 4, 1991. Governor Bob Casey appointed Harris Wofford, a member of his administration, to fill the Senate seat until a special election could be held in November of 1991.

Once appointed to the Senate seat, the Pennsylvania Democratic Party nominated Senator Wofford as the party's candidate in the special November election. The Republican candidate, Richard Thornburgh, was the former governor of Pennsylvania and then-sitting US Attorney General in the Bush administration. The polls had Senator Wofford about 10 points behind going into the last weeks of the campaign. Senator Wofford's campaign was staffed by two political consultants, Paul Begala and James Carville. They would direct the Senator to focus on the economic downturn, the fact that employees were laid off and lost their healthcare benefits and that Pennsylvania had one of the highest rates of unemployment due to reengineering. Therefore, those workers were facing a serious healthcare crisis with no insurance. Senator Wofford pulled off one of the biggest upsets seen in our political system in a long time, and the Begala-Carville strategy would become a part of Bill Clinton's Campaign for president in 1992. While the economy was the predominant factor, the results in the Pennsylvania election demonstrated that healthcare costs were a major contributor to the economy and warranted a place on the national agenda. See Fig. 7.1 regarding the rise in US healthcare expenditures since 1965.

Once Bill Clinton secured the Democratic nomination for president, his campaign slogans of "putting people first" and "It's the economy, Stupid," became strongly linked to the healthcare system. Clinton saw a direct relationship between the issues slowing the economy and increasing healthcare costs, as demonstrated by data on the rapid increase in healthcare costs, comprising nearly 13% of the gross domestic product (GDP). When compared against healthcare costs among our global competitors, it was found that the United States was spending the most. Japan was spending 6% on healthcare and all other countries spent between 6 and 13%.

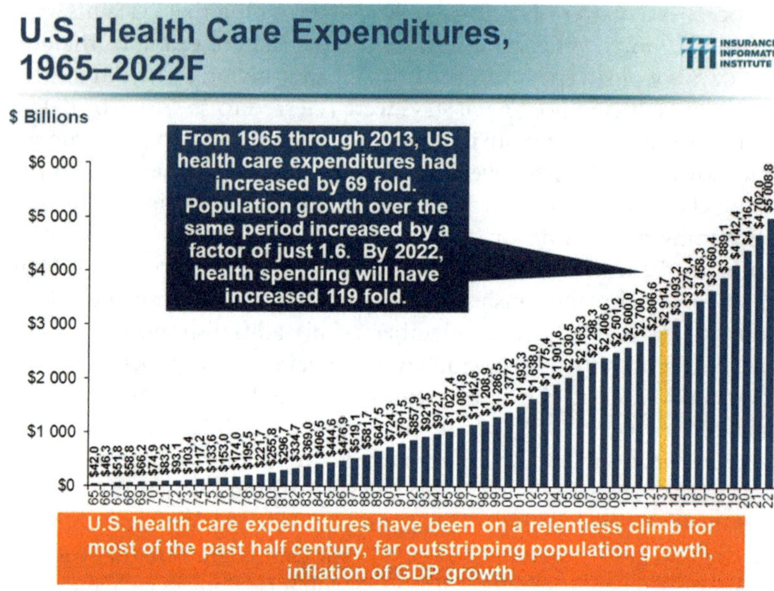

Fig. 7.1 In the late 1980s, healthcare costs made up 13% of the gross domestic product, more than any other country. Sources: Centers for Medicare & Medicaid Services, Office of the Actuary at http://www.cms.gov/Research-Statistics-Data-and-Systems/Statistics-Trends-and-Reports/NationalHealthExpendData/NationalHealthAccountsProjected.html, accessed 3/14/14; Insurance Information Institute

Clinton recognized that, in order to be competitive in the global economy, US companies had to produce products in a cost-effective way, including healthcare.

While the cost increase became linked to the economy, the Pennsylvania election brought to the fore the issue of job losses which was becoming a crisis for those whose companies had reengineered. The Clinton campaign put the issues of unemployment and healthcare on the national stage. These issues were also of great concern in the business community as it faced providing and paying for the rising cost of the healthcare benefit.

Clinton's campaign also embraced using new technology to get out their message to the computer generation. The Internet site they set up "4president.org" dealt in detail with the issue surrounding the need to reform the healthcare system. Ultimately, Clinton's campaign packaged healthcare reform as "universal access to healthcare at an affordable price." The phrase demonstrated the recognition by Clinton that the American healthcare system must find a way for every citizen to either have private health insurance or for there to be government-sponsored and directed programs like Medicare and Medicaid available to assist people who needed coverage.

Stumbling Toward the Clinton Health Access Initiative

Upon his election, President Clinton instituted a task force headed by then-First Lady Hillary Clinton to develop a healthcare plan. Unlike President Johnson and later, President Obama, the Clinton task force did not embrace the formal input of stakeholders such as the American Medical Association, American Hospital Association, the Health Insurance Association, members of Congress, and the many other national interest groups who represented healthcare practitioners and providers. Each of these groups had formal proposals on healthcare based upon the majority decision of their memberships. None were invited to participate on the task force; rather it was made up of individual healthcare practitioners, providers, suppliers, and insurers who presented the task force with their personal beliefs on reform and not those of their organized associations. In addition, the task force invited some hand-picked policy and legislative aides to join and met in closed sessions.

This strategy became a major political stumbling block for the Clinton Health Access Initiative. The reaction from the organized healthcare community and congressional committees (which were majority Democrat) on healthcare legislation was anything but supportive. Several congressional committees gave short shrift to Mrs. Clinton and were rude to Department of Health and Human Services Secretary Donna Shalala when they appeared before those committees to discuss the proposed legislation. Usually, when the congressional majority is of the same party as the president, Congress supports the legislative initiatives of the administration by holding hearings, supporting the administration's witnesses and then introducing the legislation as agreed upon by both Congress and the president. But the Clinton healthcare reform proposal, as it had been developed by the administration before congressional hearings as part of the task force findings, was introduced in Congress by the Majority Leader of the Senate and the Speaker of the House *by request*. "By request" does not connote support of the legislation—only that the administration's proposal will be considered as a courtesy. When Congress and the president of the same party agree on a program, the president will defer to Congress to develop the legislation with input from the administration. If, however, the administration does not defer to Congress and presents its own proposal, Congress of the same party as the president will offer legislation favored by the president "by request," meaning there was no congressional input and that they do so only out of respect and not support.

When the task force recommendations were reduced to legislative language and submitted in bill form, as it's table of contents indicates (see Figs. 7.2 and 7.3), it was a substantive proposal that dealt with almost every aspect of healthcare and the changes needed, in a perfect world, to begin a process to connect the private market-based health insurance

WORKING GROUP DRAFT **TABLE OF CONTENTS**

1. Introductory Overview........Page 3
2. Ethical Foundations of Health Reform ....Page 11
3. Coverage ....Page 13
4. Guaranteed National Benefit Package ....Page 19
5. National Health Board/National Administration ....Page 42
6. State Responsibilities ....Page 49
7. Regional Health Alliances ....Page 56
8. Corporate Alliances/ERISA ....Page 65
9. Health Plans ....Page 74
10. Risk Adjustment ....Page 83
11. Rural Communities in the New System ....Page 85
12. Workers Compensation and Automobile Insurance........Page88
13. Budget Development and Enforcement ....Page 93
14. Quality Management and Improvement ....Page 100
15. Information and Administrative Simplification ....Page 110
16. Protection of Privacy ....Page 122
17. Creating a New Health Workforce ....Page 125

Fig. 7.2 Page one of the table of contents for the Working Group Draft of the Clinton Health Access Initiative

WORKING GROUP DRAFT

TABLE OF CONTENTS (CONTINUED)

18. Academic Health Centers .... Page 135
19. Health Research Initiatives .... Page 137
20. Public Health Initiatives .... Page 144
21. Long-Term Care .... Page 151
22. Malpractice Reform .... Page 166
23. Antitrust Reform .... Page 169
24. Fraud and Abuse .... Page 172
25. Health Care Access Initiatives .... Page 182
26. Medicare .... Page 192
    - o Medicare Prescription Drug Benefit
27. Medicaid .... Page 200
28. Government Programs .... Page 204
    - o Department of Defense
    - o Veterans Affairs
    - o Indian Health Service
    - o Federal Employee Health Benefits Plan
29. Transition .... Page 215
    - o State Phase-In
    - o Insurance Reforms
30. Financing Health Coverage .... Page 221

Fig. 7.3 Page two of the table of contents for the Working Group Draft of the Clinton Health Access Initiative

system with government-sponsored assistance—another attempt at building a canal. The proposed plan would develop health purchasing alliances which would make available several plans for everyone's needs—whether working for a large company or needing to purchase an individual plan. The proposal would revamp the manpower pool using all practitioners at every level, deal with antitrust and malpractice concerns, and provide privacy protections and have a mandatory benefits package. It was very complicated in both size and scope (see Fig. 7.4). The table of contents of the Clinton Proposal contains reference to provisions they favored that would be a blueprint for the politics of health reform to legislate a connection

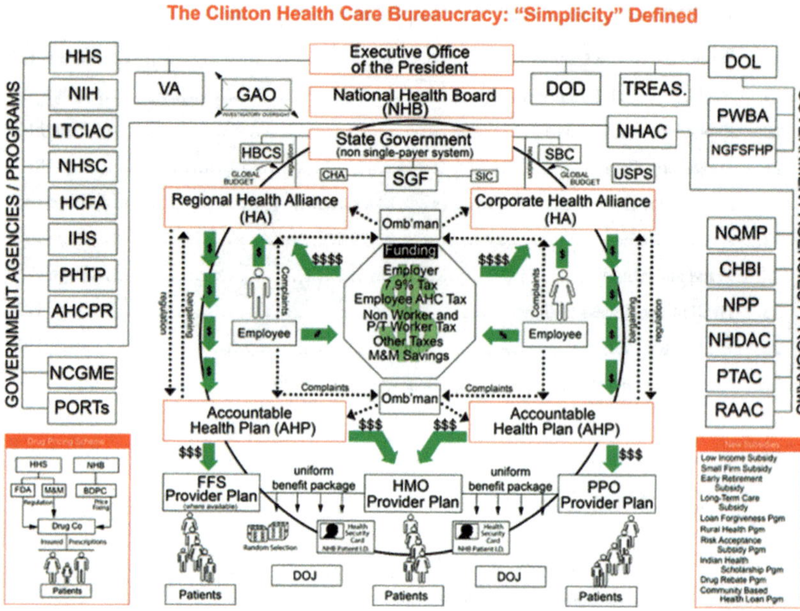

Fig. 7.4 The Clinton Health Access Initiative was complicated in both size and scope, as illustrated by this chart created by Rep. Dick Armey (R-TX). Source: https://www.motherjones.com/politics/2013/11/bill-clinton-hillary-obamacare/

between the marketplace and the right to healthcare, including provisions establishing health purchasing alliances, use of health manpower, telemedicine, and preventative services.

Like the Carter administration, the Democrats in Congress were not united behind the Clinton plan and that, coupled with intense opposition from the health insurance industry, and the opposition of every conservative think tank led to the legislation not being enacted. Even a watered-down compromise of the Clinton plan presented by Senate Majority Leader, George Mitchell (D-ME) did not gain support. Democratic Senators, including Senator Daniel Moynihan (D-NY), Chairman of the Senate Finance Committee (a major committee in any healthcare reform effort), did not agree with the Clinton proclamation of a healthcare crisis, seeing the issue as being one of insurance regulation.

Clinton Loses His Grip on Congress

By September 1994, the Clinton proposal had run its political course and could not survive the massive TV campaign of "Harry and Louise"—sponsored by the health insurance industry—which detailed for the average American family how the Clinton plan would result in big government taking over healthcare and removing coverage.[1] In addition to the faltered Congressional support, other forceful conservative political opposition and polarization as the Republicans, led by Senator Bob Dole (R-KS) dubbed the plan a liberal takeover and offered alternatives such as an individual mandate. Even though the Clinton overall reform proposal was not enacted, the debate raised awareness of the health insurance market and the growing national reaction to managed care, whereby, to reduce costs for the employer, the insurer was setting limits on types of coverage and benefits, as well as restrictions on the choice of practitioners.

In the remaining years of the Clinton presidency, many of those issues raised in the reform proposal would be discussed and, in some cases, enacted. The national attention, given the Clinton healthcare reform efforts, resulted in lingering political fallout during the 1994 midterm congressional elections. While there is no quantifiable analysis of direct correlation between the avowed opposition to the Clinton healthcare plan and the 1994 Republican takeover of the House and Senate, there can be no denying that both the debate and the opposition it generated had an impact.

The 1994 midterm elections focused on several issues: Democratic oversight of the House with issues like the House banking scandal where Democratic members were allowed to overdraft their House bank accounts without penalty and other evidence of lax control after 40 years in the majority; the very effective political plan of Representative Newt Gingrich's (R-GA) "Contract with America" detailing the problems with Democratic oversight and promising to correct them; and the lingering effect of the anti-Clinton healthcare reform effort; all of which contributed to the 1994 political tsunami where House Democrats lost 54 seats, giving the Republicans the majority with 230 seats. The loss by the Democrats was

[1] This series of television advertisements featured phrases such as "Having choices we don't like is no choice at all" and threatened a future where healthcare would be both low quality and rationed. A public archive of advertisements run by both the Republican National Committee and the Democratic National Committee can be viewed at https://www.youtube.com/watch?v=Cd_xPNT1Fh8.

so overwhelming that even Speaker of the House Tom Foley (D-WA) was defeated. Now the Clinton administration had to deal with a Republican-controlled Congress.

The Health Insurance Portability and Accountability Act (HIPAA)

The Republican Congress was not insulated from the national dialogue and exposure on healthcare. In 1996, Congress passed the Health Insurance Portability and Accountability Act (HIPAA). HIPAA provided those employees who were laid off the ability to enroll in new coverage at a subsequent job, without a new exclusion period for preexisting conditions even if they had a major illness. In addition, it helped people who lost group coverage by making them eligible to buy individual health insurance that wouldn't turn them down or exclude their preexisting conditions. However, there was a catch—to be eligible for HIPAA coverage the employee had to opt to use their COBRA coverage, which meant paying for their own health insurance. The HIPAA law was coauthored by Senators Nancy Kassebaum (R-KA) and Ted Kennedy (D-MA), the same team who previously attempted to move the country toward adopting a national healthcare system. The aim was to try and protect those laid off employees from the effects of a major illness that would constitute a preexisting condition with respect to insurance eligibility under their next employer.

In addition to the portability of the coverage, the law also included (1) several criminal sanctions to stop the fraud that was occurring in Medicare and Medicaid, (2) federal minimum standards for health insurance regulation that states were required to adopt or face federal enforcement actions, and (3) a provision instructing the president to develop a program to protect the privacy of patient medical records. The privacy provision was a minor part of the bill; nonetheless, it became the identifier for HIPAA. Although limited in scope and leading only to incremental reform, HIPAA was nonetheless significant as the first instance of Congress attempting to regulate the practice of insurers discriminating against people on the basis of preexisting conditions. Required coverage for preexisting conditions would later become a central issue in the Obama administration's efforts at healthcare reform.

The Patient's Bill of Rights

Even after the 1994 midterms, the managed care concept remained under scrutiny. In 1995, Congressman Charlie Norwood (R-GA), a dentist from Norcross, Georgia, introduced legislation referred to as the "Patient's Bill of Rights." Cosponsored by John Dingell (D-CO), the Access to Quality Care Act of 1999 would limit the scope of managed care and proscribe national standards all health insurance companies would have to meet—standards such as defining which practitioners were considered primary care physicians—as managed care plans put the primary care physician as the gatekeeper of patient care. As a cost-saving measure, if a patient needed additional care, the primary care physician would have to agree and provide a referral.

To overcome the limitation of the primary care gatekeeper, the Patient's Bill of Rights (or Patient Access to Responsible Care Act, PARCA as the second iteration was known) expanded the definition of a primary care physician to include pediatricians and obstetrician-gynecologists (OB/GYNs), removing the requirement of a referral before patients could avail themselves of those services. The law would also require removing limits on hospital stays for things like giving birth so that an overnight stay became standard for childbearing and many other medical actions. After two attempts to pass PARCA, the legislation fizzled out in 1999. It succeeded, however, in sending a message to the health insurance industry that the several limitations on covered services put in place by managed care plans needed to be changed. As a result, major health insurance companies moved to adjust their plans to do away with many of the restrictive requirements.

Medicare Part C and the Children's Health Insurance Program

The other major impact the Clinton administration had on healthcare policy and the political landscape came under the Balanced Budget Act of 1997. In cooperation with the Republican Congress, the administration negotiated changes in the Medicare and Medicaid systems, along with other budget reductions, that brought the national deficit to a surplus. The legislation made further reductions to the Medicare and Medicaid programs to gain the savings necessary to achieve a balanced budget. Among the changes was the requirement that outpatient hospital services, which were exempt from pricing via diagnosis-related groups (DRGs), be subject to a prospective payment system, referred to as Hospital Outpatient Prospective Payment (HOPP). The payment for therapy services, such as occupational therapy and physical therapy would be subject to what was referred to as a therapy cap. Thus, a Medicare patient would be allotted a predetermined amount to cover their therapeutic care. A system was devised to determine the updated payments for physician services called the Sustainable Growth Rate, or SGR. Finally, the market-based forces of healthcare would get their way in the legislation by enacting a provision called Medicare Part C.

Part C added a third section to Medicare that covered patient choice by requiring beneficiaries to choose the type of coverage they thought best for them. They could choose a Health Maintenance Organization (HMO), stay in fee-for-service Medicare and join a Part C managed care plan, opt out of Medicare and join a provider healthcare plan, or elect to have a medical savings account.

The Clinton administration did get one major change and that was to establish the Children's Health Insurance Program (CHIP) which, unlike earlier Medicaid expansions, was not an entitlement. CHIP came into being when funds from a settlement requiring tobacco companies to reimburse states for past tobacco-related costs resulted in federal Medicaid savings. The marketplace, by requiring Medicare patients to choose, would subject Medicare to the market concept of consumer choice, and a new federally supported benefit was enacted to provide health insurance to children of parents below a certain income. The resulting reduction was $156 billion from Medicare for the years 1998–2002. However, as is further discussed in Chap. 8, the implementation of those reductions such as the therapy cap, SGR, and others was delayed by congressional action each year from 1999 to 2010, so the savings were never realized, and the deficit not only reappeared but grew larger—according to the Congressional Budget Office—thanks to the Bush tax cuts in 2001 and 2003, the deficit-financed War on Terror, and the 2008 bank bailout.

A Legacy of Sexual Harassment and Hanging Chads

The remaining term of the Clinton presidency was fraught with personal turmoil resulting in his impeachment in December 1998 for perjury and obstruction of justice stemming from charges in a sexual harassment lawsuit filed against him by Paula Jones. Another star on the Clinton sexual harassment stage was Monica Lewinsky, a former White House intern with whom Clinton had had an "inappropriate" relationship. The Lewinsky affair (or not) was found to be immaterial to Jones' case. On appeal, Clinton settled the case with Ms. Jones without admitting any wrongdoing. All this is to say that the only other healthcare-related legislation accomplished by Clinton was the enactment of the Child Online Protection Act in 1998.

In 2000, Vice President Al Gore ran against George W. Bush, son of George H. W. Bush, and the election was historically close, ultimately coming down to a determination of which candidate won the state of Florida. Florida's punch-card voting system, however, was plagued by partially or inaccurately punched cards, resulting in the infamous "hanging chads." The race was so close, it went to the US Supreme Court to determine if the ballots in Florida could be recounted and letting the Florida results stand and be counted in the Electoral College. The Court determined the ballots could be recounted and, as a result, George W. Bush was elected and he took the oath of office in 2001. The next chapter discusses his administration's healthcare involvement which contained more reductions but also certain initiatives like the prescription drug program under the Medicare Modernization Act of 2003.

The impact of Clinton's personal issues and the dysfunction between his administration and Congress over healthcare led to the electorate's political reaction and gave substance to the now reenergized conservative movement, favoring the market-based approach to healthcare. Congress was in the hands of the Republicans and the conservative base becomes a force in later discussions on healthcare. Also, for the second time, the handling of the stakeholders and Congress by the Clinton and Carter administrations resulted in political backlash for healthcare policy and becomes a signal to later administrations that if you are of the same party in Congress and the White House, there needs to be close cooperation and each branch must respect the authority of the other.

Summary

Due to an economic downturn in the late 1980s and early 1990s, employers moved to adopt managed care plans which reduced costs but limited employee options. Ultimately, many corporations were unable to adequately cut costs and resorted to laying off employees. This era saw a period of reduced and managed benefits for the employees who remained and no coverage for those who were laid off. Democratic presidential candidate

Bill Clinton saw a direct relationship between the issues slowing the economy and increasing healthcare costs, as demonstrated by data on the rapid increase in healthcare costs, comprising nearly 13% of the gross domestic product (GDP) and put the issues of unemployment and healthcare on the national stage. Upon his election, President Clinton instituted a task force, headed by then-First Lady Hillary Clinton, to develop a healthcare plan. Eschewing input from Congress and other stakeholders, the task force hand-picked advisors and met in closed-door sessions, virtually guaranteeing opposition from all quarters, even within the president's own party. The largely negative national attention, given the Clinton healthcare reform efforts, resulted in lingering political fallout during the 1994 midterm congressional elections, where control of both the House and the Senate went to the Republicans. Even so, in 1996, Congress passed the Health Insurance Portability and Accountability Act (HIPAA), allowing employees to continue coverage when changing jobs. Additional progress was made near the end of the Clinton administration with the passage of the 1997 Balanced Budget Act, the enactment of Medicaid Part C and, most notably, the Children's Health Insurance Program (CHIP), providing health insurance to children of parents below a certain income threshold.

References

Access to Quality Care Act, H.R. 216. 1999.

Balanced Budget Act, Pub. L. No. 105-33, 111 Stat 251. 1997.

Child Online Protection Act, Pub. L. No. 106-310. 1998.

Children's Health Insurance Program Reauthorization Act, Pub. L. No. 111-3. 2009.

Congressional Budget Office. 1989. *The Economic and Budget Outlook: 1990–1994*. Source: Congressional Budget Office. https://www.cbo.gov/sites/default/files/101st-congress-1989-1990/reports/89-cbo-032.pdf. Accessed on July 11, 2018.

———. 2010. *An Analysis of the President's Budgetary Proposals for Fiscal Year 2011*. Source: Congressional Budget Office. https://www.cbo.gov/sites/default/files/111th-congress-2009-2010/reports/03-24-apb.pdf. Accessed on July 11, 2018.

Consolidated Omnibus Reconciliation Act, Pub. L. No. 99-272, 100 Stat 82. 1985.

Health Equity and Access Reform Today Act, S. 1770. 1993.

Health Insurance Portability and Accountability Act, Pub. L. No. 104-191. 1996.

Medicare Modernization Act, Pub. L. No. 108-173. 2003.

CHAPTER 8

Healthcare Reductions and the "Donut Hole"

Abstract Near the end of the Clinton administration, the healthcare provider community was ably demonstrating the negative impact of the reductions enacted under the Balanced Budget Act, and Congress made efforts to moderate reductions by delaying implementation. Just months after Bush II's inauguration, the terrorist attacks of September 11, 2001, put anti-terrorism initiatives at the top of the legislative agenda, but some healthcare progress was still made. Under the leadership of the Secretary of Health and Human Services, Congress passed the Medicare Prescription Drug Improvement and Modernization Act, allowing private health insurers to directly compete with Medicare. In 2005, Congress passed the Deficit Reduction Act which continued the BBA delays but also made changes to the Medicaid program. It was followed by the 2006 Tax Relief and Health Care Act which allowed another extension to delay implementation of the Sustainable Growth Rate formula, authorized an increase in Medicare Part B reimbursements for providers, and gave more flexibility to states to adapt and adopt their Medicaid programs to market forces. Near the end of Bush's second term, the country slid into recession causing many employees to again lose healthcare benefits, bringing the struggles of the uninsured and underinsured back into the spotlight.

Keywords Balanced Budget Act • Therapy cap • Medicare Prescription Drug Improvement and Modernization Act • Bush II • September 11 • Great Recession

D. F. Lavanty, *Political Aspects of Health Care*,
https://doi.org/10.1057/978-1-137-40283-7_8

Healthcare Reductions Meet with Pushback

The last year of the Clinton presidency was short on further healthcare policy. Aside from the Children's Health Insurance Program (CHIP) for the protection of children's rights, education and nutrition, most legislation dealt with global activity including the Iran Non-Proliferation Act, African Growth and Opportunity Act, Electronic Signatures in Global and National Commerce Act, and the Oceans Act. The final budget and appropriation action of the Clinton administration occurred on the District of Columbia Appropriations Bill. The bill included provisions to delay the administrative implementation of the proposed Medicare and Medicaid reductions contained in the 1997 Balanced Budget Act (BBA). While the BBA provided the Clinton administration a major healthcare success in that it included CHIP, the Clinton administration had to compromise with the Republican Congress in order to secure its inclusion. The compromise was to agree to Medicare and Medicaid reductions that would balance the US budget and have those programs subject to the Republican philosophy of market pressure by consumer choice, as seen in the Medicare Part C provision discussed in Chap. 7.

By 1999, however, the healthcare provider community was able to demonstrate the negative impact of these reductions, seen both by the Republican Congress and the Clinton administration to have been far too steep for the healthcare system to absorb. The cry was to moderate the reductions. Therefore, beginning with an added provision in an appropriations bill passed in 1999, the process of delaying the implementation of those provisions would begin. This delay action became a part of every congressional budget or appropriation action for the next several years. After the enactment of the 1997 BBA, as referred to in Chap. 7, the healthcare community, *en masse*, descended upon the Republican-controlled Congress and Clinton administration to challenge the impact of those provisions. In many cases, the healthcare associations partnered with consumer groups to lobby Congress on the impact of the reductions. The American Physical Therapy Association, the associations representing occupational therapists, respiratory therapists, and audiology therapists partnered with the American Association of Retired Persons (AARP) and other advocacy groups for the elderly to object to the $1500 therapy cap. The argument to Congress was that $1500 would not cover the cost of services needed for Medicare-eligible patients. The groups presented studies showing that if a beneficiary had a hip replacement followed by a stroke, the therapy required to facilitate recovery included physical therapy to learn to walk after the hip replacement and occupational therapy to improve speech and movement after the stroke. The costs of these therapies would far exceed the allotted $1500, and requiring the beneficiary to pay the remainder would constitute an undue burden.

The 1997 BBA reduced the amount of support for direct and indirect graduate medical education reimbursed to hospitals as part of their Medicare payments. The community of teaching hospitals would argue the reductions would wreak havoc on the residency programs. Additionally, the hospitals and their local communities brought forth data to demonstrate the Hospital Outpatient Prospective Payment (HOPP) provisions would result in significant hospital closures and would require more time for implementation.

Furthermore, the entire practitioner community, including every healthcare provider association, argued against the impact of the sustainable growth rate (SGR) formula for determining physician payments, which, if implemented would result in such major reductions in practitioner reimbursements that providers would no longer take or treat Medicare patients. The SGR would reduce, under the RBRVS formula, the conversion factor, resulting in a 4% decrease in Part B payments.[1] Congress continued to delay the implementation of that formula and would give an increase instead. The political impact of the practitioner opposition to the implementation of the 1997 SGR caused Congress to have to achieve savings to pay for the delay in implementation from other program cuts. So instead of the original savings from the 1997 SGR implementation, the delay would cost the program and Congress had to use other savings. This happened 17 times until the "doc fix" in 2014 (discussed in Chap. 9).

Medicare Part C provisions required the development of national insurance standards for indemnity and solvency, necessitating rules regarding the implementation of the Health Maintenance Organization (HMO) provision of Part C as a method of delivery of Medicare benefits. Every corner of the Medicare and Medicaid delivery system voiced concerns. The 1997 BBA also affected the rates of hospice care, home health, kidney dialysis centers, and rural hospitals. The BBA achieved, on paper at least, major direction changes in federal healthcare programs fostered by the

[1] Under the formula for Part B payment adopted in 1992 to reimburse Part B providers, all services were reimbursed one amount (the conversion factor), which, under the 1992 formula, is the amount paid.

advocates of market-based healthcare. It also demonstrated that shifting healthcare costs to the beneficiary as a result of losses incurred by a market-based system would result in pushback from patients, providers, and, in many cases, the electorate.

Bush II and the "Donut Hole" in Prescription Coverage

It was during this reactionary climate to healthcare reductions that George W. Bush, "Bush II," took office in January 2001 with the US Senate split 50/50, allowing Vice President Dick Cheney to make the tie-breaking vote when needed. The House was also held by the Republicans 222-210. With such narrow margins in both the House and Senate, close attention was needed to the concerns of the very active and important financial input of the healthcare community and its political action arms in reconciling the 1997 BBA.

With the terrorist attacks of September 11, 2001, both Congress and the president had combating terrorism as the top legislative agenda. This led to efforts to attack countries that harbored terrorists which in turn led to military action in Afghanistan and Iraq along with congressional action on the war efforts. Whatever needed to be done to deal with the aftermath of implementing or delaying provisions of the 1997 BBA, such as delaying the SGR and the therapy cap, were left to the Secretary of Health and Human Services (HHS), former Wisconsin Governor Tommy Thompson, and his department to work with the relevant congressional committees. Together they continued delaying the implementation of the 1997 BBA payment reductions in 2001 and 2002 in order to find budget offsets to cover the cost of the delays. The saving offsets would come from reductions in payments for labs tests, durable medical equipment payments, and reductions in reimbursements for imaging services.

Secretary Thompson, however, while working on BBA reduction issues became the lead in the Bush administration's effort to provide the largest change to Medicare benefits since the start of the program. When enacted in 1965, the Medicare program specifically excluded certain benefits from coverage. Interest groups such as the American Academy of Ophthalmology and the American Pharmaceutical Association lobbied to exclude benefits like dental services, and prescription drug coverage. Secretary Thompson worked with Congress to develop and pass the

Medicare Prescription Drug Improvement and Modernization Act of 2003. The law provided the elderly with a benefit that offered relief from the high cost of prescriptions and at the same time reinvented the Medicare Part C Program. The law contained provisions to allow private health insurers to directly compete with Medicare under a plan called Medicare Advantage, which provided the private insurers with Medicare reimbursement, based upon the beneficiaries' health status to provide the same services the beneficiary would have if they had stayed in traditional Medicare. The prescription plan was estimated to cost $400 billion and was taken off-budget. It was one of the biggest benefits in Medicare since its inception. Even the prescription plan itself contained market force provisions.

It should be noted that in the 1988 Catastrophic Coverage Act, all prescriptions would have been tightly regulated, but because of the input and influence of the pharmaceutical lobby, the Medicare Modernization Act passed in 2003 prohibited the Secretary from limiting or negotiating prices. No matter how a beneficiary obtained prescription coverage, the plan would allow a shared formula for prescription costs up to $2000, but for costs between $2000 and $4000 there would be no shared coverage, allowing the market to offer coverage. The lack of coverage for prescription costs between $2000 and $4000 was referred to as the "donut hole" in the program.

The Democrats in Congress opposed provisions in the prescription plan that prevented the government from capping prices, adjusting payments, and allowing the importation of prescriptions that were less costly in other countries. The Democrats saw the need for prescription coverage as proof that the government had a role in healthcare because the marketplace approach was insufficient.

President Bush was reelected in 2004 and Congress remained in Republican control as well with an increase in their majority in both Houses. Congress passed, with the support of the Bush administration, the Deficit Reduction Act of 2005 which continued the 1997 BBA delays but also made changes to the Medicaid program. The 2005 act gave more flexibility to states to adapt and adopt their Medicaid programs to market forces. It extended the look-back provision to five years for persons to be eligible for Medicaid long-term care. If assets were disposed of in that period, the state could recover them in payment for long-term case.

Long Wars and the Great Recession

In 2006, Congress passed and President Bush signed into law the Tax Relief and Health Care Act which provided again for the extension of the delay of the implementation of the SGR formula and authorized an increase in Part B reimbursements for providers. The act also expanded the use and tax impact of the development of Medical Savings Accounts designed to attract more individuals into obtaining MSAs and have more direct involvement in their healthcare needs and costs. With the nation growing a bit weary over the wars in Afghanistan and Iraq and the impending economic issues, the 2006 midterm elections were not kind to President Bush. Democrats took control of the House and the Senate with two independent members of the Senate voting with them.

In the final year of the Bush II presidency (2007–2008), the nation faced the Great Recession (2007–2013) and the legislative emphasis was on stabilizing the economy. Further healthcare changes would wait until the Obama administration was in place. During this period, many workers lost their coverage and the issue of the uninsured and underinsured became even more concerning. The next chapter discusses the effort to bring together the proponents of a market-based healthcare system and those wanting to ensure access to healthcare coverage for all citizens.

Summary

Near the end of the Clinton administration, the healthcare provider community was ably demonstrating the negative impact of the reductions enacted under the 1997 Balanced Budget Act. Congress realized that the cuts were far too steep for the healthcare system to absorb and made efforts to moderate the reductions by delaying implementation. Just months after Bush II's inauguration, the terrorist attacks of September 11, 2001, put anti-terrorism initiatives at the top of the legislative agenda, but some progress was still made with respect to healthcare. Under the leadership of the Secretary of Health and Human Services, Congress passed the Medicare Prescription Drug Improvement and Modernization Act of 2003, encompassing the greatest changes to Medicare since its inception. With Republicans continuing to look for ways to offset costs by tapping the market, the law contained provisions to allow private health insurers to directly compete with Medicare. After Bush's reelection in 2004, Congress passed the Deficit Reduction Act of 2005 that continued the 1997 BBA delays, but also made changes to the Medicaid program. It was followed by the 2006 Tax Relief and Health Care Act which provided again for the extension of the delay of the implementation of the Sustainable Growth Rate formula, authorized an increase in Medicare Part B reimbursements for providers, and gave more flexibility to states to adapt and adopt their Medicaid programs to market forces. Near the end of Bush's second term, the country slid into recession causing many employees to again lose healthcare benefits, bringing the struggles of the uninsured and underinsured back into the spotlight just in time for the Obama administration.

References

Balanced Budget Act, Pub. L. No. 105-33, 111 Stat 251. 1997.
Children's Health Insurance Program Reauthorization Act, Pub. L. No. 111-3. 2009.
Consolidated Omnibus Reconciliation Act, Pub. L. No. 99-272, 100 Stat 82. 1985.
Deficit Reduction Act, Pub. L. No. 109-171. 2005.
District of Columbia Appropriations Bill, Pub. L. No. 106-31. 1999.
Medicare Modernization Act, Pub. L. No 108-173. 2003.

CHAPTER 9

The Politics of the Affordable Care Act

Abstract President Obama's first order of duty was to stimulate the economy, but healthcare reform was not far behind. The goal of the Obama administration's healthcare initiative was to merge the market forces of the health insurance industry with a national policy providing a safety net for people who lacked health insurance. In August 2009, Senator Ted Kennedy (D-MA) passed away and his seat went to a Republican, stripping the Democrats of the 60 votes needed for cloture. The healthcare legislation was repackaged into two bills, a healthcare bill and a reconciliation bill. When both bills were signed by Obama in March 2010, the Affordable Care Act became law. The 2010 midterm elections featured every Republican candidate promising to repeal it and Republicans gained control of the House. In April 2015, Congress and the Obama administration agreed to repeal the sustainable growth rate formula replacing it with a new formula for reimbursing practitioners. In early 2016, Congress attempted to pass a bill repealing the ACA, but it was vetoed by the president. The ACA was a hot topic during the 2016 presidential election, with Republicans wanting to "repeal and replace" it and Democrats vowing to keep it. Its future is uncertain.

Keywords President Obama • Affordable Care Act • Tea Party • Obamacare • Preexisting conditions • Individual mandate

D. F. Lavanty, *Political Aspects of Health Care*,
https://doi.org/10.1057/978-1-137-40283-7_9

A Favorable Climate for Healthcare Reform

President Obama took office on the heels of the Great Recession and inherited the laws passed by Bush II to ameliorate the impact of the economic downturn by enactment of the Economic Stimulus Act to allow for tax cuts, shore up the financial markets and provide relief to the housing market. On a national basis, Obama's administration had to continue Bush II's efforts and work with Congress to enact additional legislation to pull the country out of the recession. Obama's early efforts focused on the 2009 American Recovery and Reinvestment Act designed to stimulate the economy by both maintaining existing jobs and creating new ones, and the bailout of automobile manufacturers General Motors and Chrysler via $17.4 billion in loans under the Troubled Asset Relief Program (TARP), while the manufacturers worked on restructuring. While this had to be the immediate focus of the administration, President Obama and his advisors wanted to push forward on his campaign promise to craft national healthcare legislation.

While campaigning in 2008, Obama stressed the need to find a middle of the road approach to solving the nation's healthcare issues. At the outset, the administration's goal was looking to develop a workable policy between the wide political gaps that distinguished those efforts in the past. The election of President Obama brought a favorable congressional outlook. Since the 111th Congress would provide 58 Democrats and two Independents to caucus with the Democrats the administration would have the 60 votes necessary to petition for cloture to overcome a filibuster, allowing any agreed-upon final legislation to pass both Houses of Congress. By contrast, President Clinton had only 54 Senate seats in Congress when his reform effort was attempted.

The House was also in the hands of the Democrats by a wide margin with major healthcare committees headed by representatives who had long worked on healthcare issues. The Energy and Commerce Committee and the Ways and Means Committee were chaired by Representatives Henry Waxman (D-CA) and Sander Levin (D-MI), respectively. Those two representatives, along with Representative Pete Stark (D-CA) of the Ways and Means Committee, were the House leaders in healthcare. Representatives Waxman and Stark took every opportunity at political events and speaking engagements to professional societies to advise the healthcare industry that implementing changes to healthcare would be a slow process taking many years, thus putting the advocacy groups on notice that the administration and Congress had the majorities needed to enact healthcare and that it would behoove them to work with the administration to develop that legislation.

The administration was also staffed with several people who went through the Clinton reform effort. Among them was Bill Corr serving as Deputy Secretary of Health and Human Services (HHS) under Kathleen Sebelius. Corr, who previously served as Chief of Staff for HHS Secretary Donna Shalala during the Clinton administration and as Chief Counsel for former Senate Majority Leader Tom Daschle (D-SD), was the point person for the Obama administration on healthcare reform. Along with his staff, Corr provided Obama with the historical background needed to avoid the pitfalls of the Clinton effort. Two things immediately distinguished President Obama's plan from Clinton's. First, he engaged the stakeholders at the outset and made them a part of the process. The administration secured agreements from the medical device and pharmaceutical industries that if the goal of achieving broader healthcare coverage was secured, they would have increased volume and would agree to support a tax on the additional revenue. The tax would be dedicated to offsetting subsidies made available to the underinsured or uninsured. The second difference was that the Obama administration developed a set of goals and principles guiding healthcare reform and requested that the congressional committees of jurisdiction develop legislative proposals, relying on congressional process to meet those goals.

The overall goal of the Obama administration was for Congress to enact a legislative solution on how to merge the market forces of the health insurance industry with a national policy of developing a safety net for people who lacked health insurance. The administration wanted there to be a universal package of benefits required in all insurance programs, anticipating opposition to the inclusion of coverage for certain women's health benefits, set a ceiling of a trillion-dollar program which would also reduce the deficit. The final cost of the program was the same as for the Clinton reform bill proposed 16 years earlier. Given Representative Waxman's long-standing advocacy and intimate knowledge of the Medicaid program, the administration was asking that his committee develop legislation to expand the Medicaid program to include coverage for people in lower income brackets, increasing the number of people covered by insurance overall. The administration sought to provide insurance to adult college students, and to develop a strategy to deal with pre-existing conditions.

In response to the president's goals, the House and Senate committees began the process of crafting legislation to put together an agreement that could pass a majority of the House and could be supported by the 58 Democrats and 2 independents in the Senate. The committee process began in earnest in late spring 2009 and the various proposals that were being considered for inclusion were the subject of hearings, debate, and extensive media coverage. In several areas the House and Senate bills differed; the Senate opted for a public plan, the House did not, and the Senate would rely on a general increase in taxes for financing whereas the House looked to specific taxes, such as the medical device tax.

During the 2009 August recess, members of both the House and Senate held town hall meetings on the major ideas being proposed in order to gauge national support. The meetings were well attended and, in many cases, those opposing healthcare reform became the most vocal, especially from those among the newly energized Republican political faction known as the "Tea Party."[1] They appeared at town halls and expressed concern over many elements in the proposals, but the primary focus was to oppose the individual mandate provision that would require every citizen to obtain or purchase health insurance or pay a tax penalty used to fund subsidies. A unique and significant aspect of all the town hall debates was that the complicated issues surrounding a healthcare reform effort were being discussed at length and for the first time in our political history, discussion of how the American healthcare system could be improved to accommodate competing interests was a part of the political discussion among elected officials and the electorate.

Efforts in the House and Senate

When Congress returned from recess in September 2009, it was clear that while the majority could sustain legislation to enact these changes, there were significant undercurrents, as in the past, that would maintain opposition, including that no Republicans would vote for the bill. House leadership felt the legislation that had been developed by the various committees could attract enough Democratic votes to pass and was proceeding ahead.

[1] The Tea Party movement is a conservative political movement started after President Obama's first inauguration known for its mix of conservatism, libertarianism, and populism, and being generally in favor of lower taxes and smaller government. Needless to say, not fans of government involvement in healthcare.

In the meantime, to give the effort a boost, President Obama addressed a joint session of Congress in September 2009 and urged action on the legislation, bringing a letter from Senator Ted Kennedy (D-MA) urging Congress to seize upon the historical opportunity. The reading of the letter from Senator Kennedy to Congress was the epitome of political irony. Senator Kennedy passed away on August 25, 2009, and, as a result of his passing, the 60-seat Senate majority needed to insure a positive outcome in the Senate was in doubt. The proposed healthcare reform legislation became dependent on his replacement, which proved to be a major political challenge.

By November, the various House committees completed their action and a final bill was brought to the full House. Some of the major provisions in President Obama's bill were (1) a requirement that states develop buying cooperatives to preserve the health insurance marketplace, (2) all citizens would be required to purchase health insurance, (3) insurers must provide a basic mandatory package of benefits in all plans, including women's health coverage for well visits, preventive care, family planning, and contraception, and (4) the legislation would provide funding to the states for 100% funding for three years and 90% thereafter to grow coverage for their Medicaid programs to expand the range of income eligibility for Medicaid. Also, except for the Medicaid funding, the Affordable Health Care Act was very similar to the Republican alternative to the Clinton Plan sponsored by Senator Bob Dole. The legislation passed the House in November by a vote of 220–215, a margin of 5 votes and another signal that the administration was again treading on political uncertainty, with 40 members of the Democratic majority, who faced close reelection in an off-year presidential election and opposition from a well-financed and vocal "tea party" voting against the legislation.

In the Senate, Paul Kirk (D-MA) had been appointed by the Governor of Massachusetts to fill the seat of Senator Kennedy until a special election was held in January 2010. During November and December, the Senate Finance and Senate Health, Education, Labor and Pensions (HELP) Committees finished their markups and after adding several amendments to keep the 60-member majority in line, a final bill was sent to the Senate, where it passed on December 23, 2009, by a 60-39 vote with all Republican members opposed. The Senate bill retained many of the House provisions, but the method of raising the tax revenue needed to support the legislation was very different. The House-passed bill relied on a tax increase in certain areas to cover the program subsidies, but the Senate bill proposed raising revenues by taxing what were called “Cadillac healthcare plans” that had high options of coverage through employment but had been opposed in the House. The bottom line was, in January 2010, the House and Senate would have to meet in a conference committee to work out the differences and be able to attract at least 218 House votes while keeping the 60 Senate votes.

In the January 2010 Massachusetts special election, Scott Brown, the Republican candidate to fill the seat of Senator Kennedy, won an unexpected come-from-behind race against the Democratic candidate, current Massachusetts Attorney General Martha Coakley. Like the 1991 special election upset in Pennsylvania with Senator Wofford changing the healthcare landscape during President Clinton’s effort, another political upset changed the course of President Obama and the Democratic Congress’ efforts on healthcare reform. With the election and seating of Senator Brown (R-MA) the Senate was composed of 57 Democrats, two Independents who vote with the Democrats for a potential total of 59 and no longer the number needed to obtain a cloture vote to stop a filibuster. In February, congressional leaders and the administration decided to move ahead by having the House pass the Senate bill on healthcare reform (the Patient Protection and Affordable Care Act) which contained provisions not in the original House bill.

Swift Political Maneuvering

In order to solve some of the differences and maintain a 218-member vote in House, the decision was made to pass a budget reconciliation bill. Under the Budget and Impoundment Control Act of 1974 and its amendments, a budget reconciliation bill in the Senate, once it met the provisions of reductions required, would need only a simple majority to pass. Therefore, the House crafted a reconciliation bill called the Healthcare and Education Reconciliation Act of 2010 that included subjects that were acceptable in the budget process. The changes met the criteria for the Senate to be able to consider the bill under their budget rules requiring only a 51-vote majority. The House then proceeded in March 2010 to pass the reconciliation bill that contained changes to the Senate-passed healthcare reform bill, most notably the funding mechanism of the Cadillac tax being delayed for several years and funding to close the “donut hole” in Bush II’s 2003 prescription drug plan. The House bill would eliminate the hole, but the Senate bill did not. So, adding those provisions would keep those House members who opposed the Senate version on board.

If one wants to view the pure political aspects of healthcare, one need only review and understand the action by the Democratic Congress having passed these two bills, one the Senate-passed health reform bill and the other a budget reconciliation bill to get the Affordable Healthcare Act (ACA) into law.

Several members of the House recognized that they could leverage their votes to get additional provisions added to the legislation. One example was in the medical device tax. The original House-passed bill set the device tax at 2.8% on only the more expensive and sophisticated medical devices. In order to get one member from New York to vote for passage of both bills, the leadership agreed to reduce the tax 2.3% and expand the application of the tax to all medical devices, representing a major departure in the medical device industry. In the final analysis, the House passed two bills, the Senate healthcare bill and a reconciliation bill, followed by the Senate passing the reconciliation bill. When both were signed by President Obama in March 2010 the ACA became law.

Is It Affordable? Does Anyone Care? The ACA Encounters Opposition

At this point in time, significant media coverage of all the legislative maneuvering resulted in very vocal opposition to the law. As with large-scale changes in healthcare policies in the past, the characterization of the ACA by those opposed to it and by the media had a significant impact on the outcome of national elections. The 2010 congressional elections saw a surge in Republicans in the House, similar to the sweep that occurred during the Clinton healthcare reform effort. The Democrats went from 235 House members to 193 while Republicans membership rose to 242. The election gave real impetus to the conservative “Tea Party” movement which was greatly opposed to the healthcare reform law. The major issue of every Republican candidate for national office became the repeal of the ACA, which they dubbed “Obamacare” in an effort to negatively brand the issue.

The Senate remained in the hands of the Democrats for now, but Republicans would take it over in the 2014 midterm elections. With both houses of Congress in Republican hands, President Obama retained the ability to veto legislation attempting to repeal the ACA, and indeed he did.

In April of 2010 and for the following six years, various provisions of the law needed to be implemented. The process of implementation encountered many difficulties prompting a new round of media coverage and political discourse on the pitfalls of the ACA. The constitutionality of the law was challenged in *National Federation of Independent Business v. Sebelius* and although the Supreme Court determined that the basis of the law was constitutional, the Court also found that the federal government could not coerce the states to follow the Medicaid expansion requirement designed to raise the qualifying income level to cover more people. That provision would have given the states more funding for three years if they increased the poverty level to cover more uninsured. Most of the states with Republican-controlled legislatures or governors, based upon the ruling of the Supreme Court, opted out of the Medicaid requirement, could not gain coverage and would rely on those insurance plans offered throughout the federal system.

State-based insurance buying cooperatives also needed to be implemented to give residents an opportunity to choose a private health insurance plan. Like the Medicaid expansion, most Republican-controlled states did not develop buying cooperatives, leaving the federal government to establish them instead. With so many people turning to the federal exchange, when the online system opened for business, the computer program enabling people to shop insurance programs crashed due to the large volume of users logging on simultaneously. This incident provided another anti-ACA media-feeding frenzy seized upon by those opposed to the law, bringing into focus yet again the political struggle the United States faces regarding healthcare reform.

Another hiccup on the road to implementation arose from the requirement that all health insurance plans cover preexisting conditions. There would have to be a redistributive impact and every part of the program had to work to have the preexisting conditions coverage properly funded. When an insurance plan is forced to cover a costly risk because the policyholder is known to have a health-related condition, the insurer must offset the additional costs by raising the rates of other policy holders in order to remain profitable. The effect of requiring insurers to cover preexisting conditions was that health insurance coverage costs increased across the board, adding more fuel to the fire of those opposed to the ACA. Keep in mind that the individual mandate was put in place to prevent this from happening. If everyone has insurance, the risk/cost is spread among a larger group, keeping costs down.

Reductions, Payments, and Reimbursements

While the ACA was the major topic of political discussion from 2010 to 2016, Congress and the administration had to deal with preventing reductions in physician's payments as a result of the sustainable growth rate (SGR) adopted under the 1997 Balanced Budget Act (BBA). As in the Bush II administration, Congress under Obama used several different legislative vehicles to delay the implementation of the SGR-based reduction until 2015. This was referred to as the annual "doc fix." Finally, in April 2015, Congress and the Obama administration came to an agreement that, notwithstanding the cost of $141 billion, the formula had to be repealed and passed the Medicare Access and CHIP Reauthorization Act repealing the 1997 SGR provision and replacing it with a new formula for reimbursing practitioners under Medicare with a merit-based incentive system. The new formula set a fixed five-year increase (until 2020) and directed the Centers for Medicare and Medicaid Services (CMS) to craft future reimbursement models based upon pay-for-performance and for accountable care organizations to alter the fee-for-service model historically used in Medicare and Medicaid.

Both Congress and the administration, while focusing on the macro-political strife being aired on the ACA, still had to deal with preserving access to physician care under Medicare. In light of the political influence of the healthcare provider community, it's local political networks and political action committees, Congress and the administration responded to their continued advocacy to solve the SGR reimbursement issue, showing a limited willingness for the 114th Congress and the administration to work together to solve some healthcare policy issues.

Repeal? Replace? Amend?

On the macro issue, however, Congress and the administration remained far apart. In January of 2016, Congress passed the Restoring Americans' Healthcare Freedom Reconciliation Act of 2015 intending to repeal parts of the ACA and sent it to the president for approval. President Obama vetoed the act, alleging that it would harm both the health and financial security of millions of Americans. The ACA remained the law of the land. In the 2016 congressional elections, sitting Republican members seeking reelection and Republicans running to unseat Democratic members, campaigned again on the promise that, if elected they would vote to repeal the ACA.

During the 2016 presidential election, Republican candidate Donald Trump campaigned on a platform of repealing and replacing "Obamacare." On the other side of the aisle, Democratic candidate Hillary Clinton, architect of the Clinton-era healthcare reform effort, campaigned on the position that the ACA should remain the law, but should be amended to correct some elements.

As the 115th Congress took office in January 2017, and the Trump administration was sworn in, the American healthcare system continued to be a major political issue as well as a constantly moving target among the electorate. The text throughout these nine chapters has demonstrated how the political climate of each era determined the type and extent of the programs that were enacted. When politically favorable, universal approval for all programs prevailed, but when political retrenchment occurred, more marketplace forces prevailed. In the future enactment of healthcare policy, the political aspects of the time will again direct the majority party the opportunity to shepherd a national healthcare program deemed suitable for a majority of the American electorate.

Summary

Elected on the heels of the Great Recession, President Barak Obama's first order of duty was to stimulate the economy, but with both houses of Congress enjoying Democratic majorities, and a host of healthcare reform experts and allies in their ranks, it was only a matter of time before the administration got to work on pursuing its campaign promise of enacting national healthcare legislation. The overall goal of the Obama administration's healthcare initiative was to merge the market forces of the health insurance industry with a national policy providing a safety net for people who lacked health insurance. Although there were minor disagreements in the House and Senate versions of the legislation, it seemed destined to pass given the Democratic majorities. But in August 2009, Senator Ted Kennedy (D-MA) passed away and his seat went to a Republican, stripping the Democrats of the 60 votes needed for cloture. To get around this, the healthcare legislation was repackaged into two bills, a healthcare bill and a reconciliation bill. When both bills were signed by President Obama in March 2010 the Affordable Care Act (ACA) became law. Republicans were very vocal in their opposition to Congress' swift maneuvering to get the ACA passed, and the 2010 midterm elections featured every Republican candidate promising to repeal it. Enough Republicans were elected to give them control of the House. Democrats managed to hold on to the Senate until 2014. Still looming was the issue of preventing reductions in physician's payments as a result of the sustainable growth rate (SGR) adopted under the 1997 Balanced Budget Act (BBA). Like his predecessors, Obama had employed various tactics to delay SGR implementation. In April 2015, Congress and the Obama administration agreed to repeal the SGR formula replacing it with a new formula for reimbursing practitioners. There was little bipartisan cooperation on other matters, however, and, in early 2016, Congress attempted to pass a bill repealing the ACA, but it was swiftly vetoed by the president. The ACA was a hot topic during the 2016 presidential election, pitting Republican candidate Donald "Repeal and Replace Obamacare" Trump against Democratic candidate Hillary "Keep it and Tweak it" Clinton, with Trump emerging the victor.

A Note on the Future of Healthcare Policy

In the first several chapters, we see how the positive response of the political process helped usher in the enactment of the Medicare and Medicaid program and allow, for the first time, a role for the federal government in healthcare policy. The positive response continued to allow Congress to enact programs to expand the infrastructure with education, construction, and research programs but did not allow Congress to change the fee-for-service insurance concept. As costs rose, Congress was faced with the process of how to reduce those costs and still maintain benefits in the Medicare and Medicaid programs. The middle chapters dealt with the politics of cost containment throughout the budget reconciliation process. However, during both those periods a segment of the political process called for universal healthcare, abandoning marketplace forces and extending coverage to all which clearly reflects the dichotomy of healthcare as a right versus an option. Finally, we discussed that when a comprehensive program was proposed or enacted, there was significant backlash from the political process.

Does the new administration and Congress possess the tools necessary to build a connection—the canal connecting the Nile and Amazon rivers—between the inherent conflicts in our healthcare system and address each individual voter's personal concern about what access to affordable quality healthcare really means? To be sure, the political aspects of our healthcare system will be a topic of discussion and debate for generations to come. Hopefully, past reform efforts can provide some political direction for future efforts on the best way forward.

References

American Recovery and Reinvestment Act, Pub. L. No. 111-5. 2009.
Balanced Budget Act, Pub. L. No. 105-33, 111 Stat 251. 1997.
Consolidated Omnibus Reconciliation Act, Pub. L. No. 99-272, 100 Stat 82. 1985.
Economic Stimulus Act of 2008, Pub. L. No. 110-185. 2008.
Emergency Economic Stabilization Act of 2008, Pub. L. No. 110-343. 2008.
Health Care and Education Reconciliation Act, Pub. L. No. 111-152. 2010.
Medicare Modernization Act, Pub. L. No. 108-173. 2003.
National Federation of Independent Business v. Sebelius, 567 U.S. 519. 2012.
Patient Protection and Affordable Health Care Act, Pub. L. No. 111-148. 2010.
Restoring American Health Care and Freedom Act of 2015, H.R. 3762, 114th Cong. 2016.

Index

D. F. Lavanty, *Political Aspects of Health Care*,
https://doi.org/10.1057/978-1-137-40283-7

9781137406200